Chemistry for Space Settlement

David A. Dietzler

Table of Contents

Preface

In my three previous books, <u>Mining the Moon: Bootstrapping Space Industry</u>, <u>Space Enterprise</u>, and <u>Building Spaceships</u>, I discussed some of the resources and manufacturing challenges of space settlement. In this book we will go into more detail concerning chemistry and metallurgy for space industry and settlement. This author has no doubt that space energy and the exploitation of lunar materials and helium 3 resources are vital to the survival and growth of the human species, but others may not be convinced. Mars settlement and free space settlement are also very important. Eventually, woman and man may populate the solar system and even reach the stars. We have only taken our first steps into space. Let's hope that the journey lasts a long time, and that it will help deliver the Earth and all the human, animal and plant life here from extinction. By creating a multi-planet, even multi-solar system, civilization and abode of life, even a super volcano or another ice age couldn't kill off all humans as well as our pets and a huge number of wild creatures and plants on land and in the sea.

Space Industry, Climate Change and Our Future on and off Earth

Climate change due to greenhouse gas releases by human activity is undeniable. Even if there is a natural component to global warming there is no reason to aggravate the situation with industrial emissions and the effects of agriculture. If sea level rise becomes a problem, billions of dollars of coastal property might be lost even with aggressive and costly sea wall building programs. Marginal lands and deserts could be fertilized and irrigated for the planting of crops and trees that can sink carbon dioxide and repair some of the damage that has been done, but that too will be very expensive. Where would all the fresh water come from? Dams, canals and aqueducts could be built. Wells could be drilled. Seawater could be desalinated, but that would be energy intensive and costly. Feeding, clothing and housing the world's population in the next 30 years and beyond will require huge water projects and cultivating of marginal and desert lands even without climate change. The really frightening thing about climate change is that it will probably change rain fall patterns in unpredictable ways. Rich farmland could become dry and worthless, but some dry areas might become wetter. Irrigating and farming now barren lands could effect the climate and rainfall patterns too. About the only thing we can be sure of is that man made greenhouse gas emissions must be curtailed.

Electrical power production must be decarbonized, otherwise electric cars and electric furnaces will just shift carbon dioxide emissions from tail pipes and home chimneys to power plant smokestacks. Even by replacing coal with natural gas, a fuel that emits half as much CO_2 as coal burning does, electrification of transportation, industry and heating would still mean more greenhouse gas emissions. It is not necessary to condemn the internal combustion engine or the external combustion engine (e.g. steam turbines for ships). Jets, small planes, trucks, railroad trains, ships, farm machinery and construction machinery all have advantages over electric versions like greater speed, range, power and cargo capacity, and they could run on carbon neutral biofuel derived from algae, plant sources and wastes. Biofuels can be pumped to fill tanks much faster than batteries can be recharged, and they can be transported via existing pipeline and tanker truck/ship/railroad car infrastructure. Filling stations could easily be adapted to biofuels. They are energy dense and liquid at ordinary temperatures. They do not require cryogenic dewars or exotic storage tanks and materials. Engines running on biofuels won't endure the severe loss of power and range at low temperatures that afflicts batteries.

Cement making generates a lot of CO_2 from the gas that is burned to heat the limestone and shale to the CO_2 that is released when the limestone decomposes. It should be possible to use electric heat instead of natural gas and sequester the carbon from the limestone. Steel making releases lots of carbon from the burning coke in blast furnaces. Blast furnaces could be replaced by Direct Reduced Iron furnaces that use electricity, hydrogen and carbon monoxide. The CO_2 that is still produced when the CO reduces the iron ore and the limestone flux breaks down could be sequestered. It might be possible to make CO from biological sources, like the incomplete combustion of biofuels. This would be carbon neutral. Heat for oil refining could be electrical since there will still be some petroleum in the future for petrochemicals to make plastics, drugs, paint, dyes, synthetic fibers, lubricants, etc. When all the economically recoverable petroleum is exhausted, we can switch to chemicals made from natural gas and coal. This will still require carbon free electricity and extreme caution to prevent methane emissions in the form of natural gas releases. Methane is twenty-one times more potent at trapping heat than CO_2. Besides emissions from natural gas well leaks there are methane emissions from farms. Agricultural emissions might be reduced by planting cover crops and spraying fields with compost.

Decarbonizing electrical production and switching to electric cars, electric home furnaces and electric industrial process heat as well as supplying carbon free electricity for commercial building lighting, heating and kitchens can only be achieved by switching to renewable energy sources like ground based solar, winds, geothermal, waves, tides, hydro, biofuels and carbon free nuclear fission. Conservation will also be important. Solar and wind are intermitted power sources that require storage systems for the times when the Sun doesn't shine and the wind doesn't blow. At night there is no

Sun but the winds can still blow; even so, energy storage will be necessary if we make extensive use of solar and wind energy. Home rooftop solar installations will come with batteries. Large scale solar and wind generation will require storage in the form of pumped hydro, compressed air energy storage, hydrogen from water electrolysis and spikes in demand could be handled by batteries and flywheels. The biggest problem with solar is that sometimes the sky is overcast and the Sun doesn't shine for weeks on end. The wind can still blow, but a large investment in these intermittent power sources will require a costly investment in power storage. If the Sun doesn't shine in the dead of winter for weeks it might be possible to fire up old natural gas or coal fired power plants if everybody remains connected to the grid and the old fossil fuel plants are preserved, but will there be any fuel available if the renewable energy industry has replaced all the fossil fuel businesses?

Fusion and space solar power satellites (SSPS) could supply power to the grid with zero carbon emissions 24/7 regardless of the weather and season of the year without expensive storage systems. These are long term solutions. Commercial nuclear fusion is decades away. The fusion of deuterium and tritium releases floods of high energy neutrons that could lead to the generation of small amounts of low level nuclear waste. The neutrons might also damage the reactor after some time of operation and ruin the economics of this power source. Deuterium-deuterium fusion also produces neutrons. Deuterium and helium 3 fusion releases no neutrons except for a small number generated by deuterium-deuterium side reactions in the plasma. Helium 3 fusion with helium 3 is truly aneutronic. No low level waste. No reactor damage. The only problem is that helium 3 reactors are way beyond present technology that hasn't even achieved commercial deuterium-tritium fusion. Also, there is next to no helium 3 on Earth. The only source is from tritium decay in nuclear warheads. However, there is helium 3 on the Moon and it could be mined. The helium 3 comes from the solar wind which is deflected by Earth's geomagnetic field, thus, none of it makes it to Earth. The Moon has no magnetic field so it is blasted by the solar wind and helium 3 along with traces of hydrogen, carbon, nitrogen and normal helium 4 are implanted into the Moon's soil, or regolith. Machines that dig up regolith and roast it in onboard furnaces could drive off the helium 3 and other elements. The helium 3 is only present in parts per billion, so about one square kilometer of lunar territory would have to be dug to a depth of about 3 meters to produce 33 kg. of the stuff. [1] To power the USA more than 30 tons of it would be needed every year. Tens of thousands of tons of mining machines would be needed and these would be very expensive to ship to the Moon. In my earlier book, Mining the Moon: Bootstrapping Space Industry 3rd edition, I discussed sending a thousand tons of "seed" machines to the Moon to build up a mining and manufacturing base using on-site resources to support a SSPS building program. It might also be possible to build up industry to create helium 3 mining machine construction factories on the Moon that use on-site resources of metals and other elements.

We don't know if we will ever get commercial nuclear fusion of any kind much less helium 3 fusion, but let's hope we do. Since such a fusion reactor cannot meltdown and even if it exploded it would not release radioactive material, and it doesn't generate nuclear waste, it could be built in the heart of a city and supply heat by way of a steam loop to buildings as well as electricity. This would be very efficient and of great benefit in northern cities which will endure brutal winters even if the planet warms up by a few degrees. Many northern cities in North America, Europe and Russia don't get much solar power especially in winter and they don't get much wind. Helium 3 fusion would be ideal.

Solar power satellites don't come with the added benefit of ample cheap waste heat, but solar power is a rather mature technology. Presuming that it would be affordable to bootstrap up space industry launched with SpaceX and/or Blue Origin rockets in the future, it should be possible to supply raw materials with mass driver lunar launchers and mass catcher spacecraft to SSPS builders in space. In my vision, there is one major obstacle—we have never built anything as gigantic as a miles wide powersat in space. Can we do it? In weightlessness or micro-gravity with no wind, no waves and no ground movement it seems it should be possible to build enormous structures. Some have even envisioned mega-scale engineering projects like solar shields to cool Venus or a Dyson sphere around the Sun. This is a job for architects, bridge builders and ship builders if we can put them to work on things even bigger than the Golden Gate Bridge or super tankers. There is no physical reason these SSPSs can't be built. The engineering knowledge just doesn't exist but it could be developed.

It won't be any good if we can industrialize space for less than $40 billion only to discover that we can't build giant structures in any practical way. I envisioned $10 billion for a 1000 ton lunar industrial "seed" and perhaps another $10 billion for the orbital stations where the powersats are built in addition to a few billion dollars to transport skeleton crews to GEO and the Moon. Most of the work would be done by robots. With no experience in mega-scale astro-engineering, will any reasonable persons or corporations take the risk?

Helium 3 fusion and SSPSs are like two birds in the bush. Many would say that nuclear fission is the bird in the hand. Nuclear power plants are expensive and they present dangers that many people want no part of. If we do choose space energy it will probably only be after more decades of research and development in space and in the field of nuclear fusion. In the meantime, nuclear fission could serve as a bridge to the clean energy future. Then we must ask, do we want to shoot for helium 3 mining on the Moon or SSPSs construction? Why not both? The global demand for energy will continue to grow. A thousand SSPSs each rated at 5 GWe could only supply a part of that demand. How long would it take to build one powersat much less a thousand of them? Helium 3 fusion could make a big contribution not only of electricity but also heat. Other forms of renewable energy like ground based solar, winds, waves, tides, geothermal, biofuels and such combined with storage and conservation, could supply energy too. It looks like there will be a market for whatever green energy technology you want to put your money into from wind to space energy.

Economics will decide what happens even if it does prove possible to build gigantic powersats and fuse helium 3. Financial competition with ground based renewable energy might make space energy a loser. That would be unfortunate. Profit making space enterprises could grow beyond energy and build large space stations in equatorial low Earth orbit (ELEO) with private condos, time shares and hotels within for tourists. Some break-through in micro-gravity manufacturing might make orbital factories a reality. There could be lunar tourism, space settlement and cities on the Moon, Mars and in free space. Eventually, we could reach the stars.

The Earth would not be abandoned and population growth would not cause the extinction of whales, elephants and grizzly bears. Green energy would put an end to pollution and global warming. As living standards rise population growth rates will decrease. At some point the human population will stabilize and perhaps even shrink. While it is possible that the resources of space like the asteroids could be used to build free space settlements that support a population thousands of times greater than that on Earth, many people may not be interested. There could be people who choose to remain childless and people who choose to breed. A balance would exist that either stops growth or allows it to continue at a much lower rate. Fears of a human galactic infestation that resembles a plague of locusts stripping away all the natural wonders of space and replacing them with apartment complexes are unfounded. Man and woman will learn to live without their wasteful ways or we will never make it off the planet.

The Moon and Mars have plenty of metals, glass, basalt and feedstock for ceramics. Many of the things now made of plastic can be made of these materials, but not everything. One of the biggest challenges for space industry and settlement is the lack of oil, coal and natural gas on the Moon and Mars. These are not desirable for fuel in space, but they could supply chemicals for synthetic materials and other products if they existed. There are other sources of necessary elements like hydrogen, carbon and nitrogen to make synthetic fibers, rubber washers, plastic O-ring seals, pipe dope, adhesives, duct tape, electrical tape, flexible hoses and tubing, sealants, caulk, gaskets, lubricants, plastic toys, polycarbonate space helmets, spacesuits from nylon, PET, Kevlar and other synthetic materials, electrical wire insulation, varnish for electric motor coils, rubber gloves and PPE, disposable medical supplies, food wrapping, preservatives, paint, dyes, inks, drugs, resins and many other products. There are solar wind implanted elements including hydrogen, carbon and nitrogen in the lunar regolith. Water, carbon dioxide and ammonia have been detected in polar ices. These resources are sparse and anything made from them must be recycled. The Martian atmosphere contains CO_2, nitrogen and argon. There seems to be water in permafrost. There are vast amounts of CO_2 and water frozen in the polar caps. Carbonaceous asteroids contain water and a tarry hydrocarbon material resembling kerogen that could someday provide vast amounts of light elements (H,C,N) to the Moon and free space settlements. Beyond that, the ices of the moons of the outer planets and even the atmospheres of the Gas Giants and Ice Giants could supply light elements, especially hydrogen and helium 3 which is more plentiful in the atmospheres of the giant planets than on the Moon. Everything made from light elements used on the Moon and Mars and in free space settlements as well as other worlds must be rigorously reused and recycled. It might seem like the atmospheres of the outer planets contain endless supplies of light elements, but it will be a long time before those resources are tapped and even then it will take a lot of money, machinery and energy to get those elements. We will start out with solar wind implanted volatiles and polar ices on the Moon. These only exist in traces and huge amounts of regolith will have to be processed to get them. It will be essential for the success of lunar and Earth orbital industry for the use of plastic and such to be reduced with metal, basalt and glass substitutes and to reuse and recycle all synthetic materials even worn out clothing and old spacesuits. Disposable culture won't make it in space.

Mars seems rich compared to the Moon when it comes to light elements. Even so, it will probably not be as easy to extract those elements from the atmosphere and ices of Mars as it is to get them from oil, coal and gas on Earth. The Mars settlers will be wise to be as tight with their plastic supplies as the Lunans are. Earthlings might be much better at reducing, reusing and recycling too in the highly populous, oil depleted future.

Let's suppose that space industry and energy in the future is viable from a business point of view and that space settlement occurs. I have discussed some of that in previous books. How will chemists tackle the production of all sorts of materials from steel to polyethylene in space? That will be the main focus of this book. Our future on and off Earth may depend on this.

Lunar Resources

Notes on Lunar Geology

The Moon is thought to have formed by the accretion of material splashed out of the primordial Earth by a giant impact with another body. It is less dense than the Earth and seems to contain fewer heavy metals like iron. Low boiling point elements like sodium and potassium are depleted. The surface has been bombarded, pulverized and homogenized by eons of meteoric impacts. There has never been air, liquid water or life on the Moon, thus, there is no wind or water erosion and no material of biological origin. The particles of soil, regolith, are not weathered and they are very sharp and abrasive. There are no sedimentary rocks like limestone, hematite, bauxite or pitchblende and thus little or no concentrations of rocks that could be classified as ores.

The dark seas of the Moon, the mare, are plains of hardened lava that have been powdered by impacts. They consist mostly of basalt which is composed of iron-magnesium silicates like olivine and pyroxene along with feldspar consisting mostly of the calcium-aluminum silicate mineral called anorthosite. There is also ilmenite, an iron-titanium oxide, in varying concentrations from place to place. The lighter areas, called the Highlands because they are elevated above the basins that filled with lava to become the mare, are made mostly of anorthosite. Unlike the Earth, there is very little albite, a sodium-aluminum silicate, and very little potassium feldspar. Granite is very rare on the Moon too.

The Riches of the Moon

The Moon, sitting in a gravity well only 1/21 as deep as Earth's, could supply millions of tons of oxygen, raw regolith, basalt, ceramics, glass, silicon, iron, calcium, aluminum, magnesium, titanium, sodium, sulfur, potassium, manganese, chromium, volatiles and more annually for construction in outer space. Uranium, thorium and rare earth elements exist on the Moon and the possibility of undiscovered igneous ore bodies of magmatic or volcanic origin sparks the imagination. Ice in permanently shadowed polar craters could supply water, carbon monoxide, carbon dioxide, ammonia and possibly other substances. Rockets would be used to transport mining equipment, metal extraction and materials processing devices and manufacturing machines like 3D printers, large engine lathes and assembly robots to the Moon. The Moon base would be built up with local resources. This is called in-situ resource utilization or ISRU. Machinery, habitat, vehicles and more will be made on the Moon using an initial stock of carefully selected machines to expand the base and replicate machinery. This is called *bootstrapping*. Once the base is built up an electromagnetic mass driver launcher will shoot payloads of regolith and other materials into space for construction. This will not be the end of the Moon base. Lunar industry will continue to expand and multiple settlements will be established on the Moon connected by dirt roads and railways.

Besides physical materials, the Moon offers a number of unique resources. There is free vacuum for establishing super clean environments, purifying and evaporating materials, and making things without contamination from atmospheric moisture, oxygen and nitrogen. Rust, corrosion, storms, lightning strikes, floods, forest fires and other Earthly woes are non-existent on the Moon. Low gravity makes it possible to move heavy loads around without as much manpower or horsepower. Loads on machinery and bearings will be reduced. Solar energy is available reliably for two weeks at a time, never obscured by clouds, at lower latitudes and in polar regions it is available up to 90% of the time. Solar energy can be used to generate electricity or it can be concentrated with parabolic mirrors to produce high temperatures for melting materials. Super cold temperatures can be obtained with shielded space radiators exposed only to the 4K temperature of outer space. This makes it possible to liquefy oxygen, hydrogen, helium and other gases with ease.

There are a few disadvantages. The lunar surface is soaked in radiation and it experiences temperature extremes. During the extreme heat of day, vehicles and mining machines could be parked under aluminized Mylar plastic parasols. Heating systems will be needed for machinery in the supercold of lunar nightspan so the metals don't crack. These heating systems might use electricity from solar panels and batteries or fuel cells, tanks of molten salts, or nuclear energy. Keeping humans alive will require pressurized habitat and complex life support systems. Habitat can be covered with several meters of regolith for radiation shielding, thermal insulation and micrometeoroid protection. Most work "outdoors" could be done by AI and teleoperated robots instead of spacesuited workers. Regolith seems to be a great resource, but much of it consists of a very fine dust made of sharp abrasive particles that could work their way into mechanical systems and cause things to wear out rapidly. When crews return from the outdoors they could bring in dust that if inhaled will harm the lungs. Airlocks with wash down systems and turtle-back spacesuits could counteract the dust problem. The dust might become useful as an abrasive grit after sieving and sizing for grinding and polishing metal and glass items. The low gravity could reduce burdens on men and machinery, but it could also lead to bone and muscle atrophy during long term stays on the Moon. Humans have endured prolonged weightlessness, but nothing is known about the effects of partial gravity on humans, animals or plants. We don't want humans to be debilitated by low G, and we don't want problems with farming livestock and crops. There is more to learn about life in low gravity on the Moon and other worlds of the solar system.

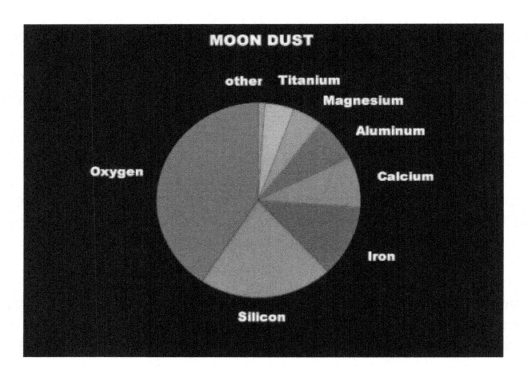

Fig. 1 Lunar soil or Moon dust, technically called regolith, contains many useful elements for survival and industry on the Moon and in outer space.

Lunar soil, regolith, or Moon dust is mostly oxygen and silicon along with iron, calcium, aluminum, magnesium, titanium and traces of chromium, manganese, sodium, potassium, phosphorus, sulfur and tiny amounts of many other elements. It also contains traces of hydrogen, helium, methane, CO, CO_2 and nitrogen implanted by the solar wind that can be extracted by mining millions of tons of regolith and heating it to about 700 C. Numerous processes for extracting and separating these elements have been described. Ideally, it should be possible to heat regolith until it decomposes and separate the elements with something similar to a mass spectrometer. Dr. Peter Schubert of Purdue University has designed a device that heats and decomposes regolith into oxygen and other elements like iron, aluminum, titanium and silicon. These are all separated in what he calls an "All Isotope Separator" that resembles a mass spectrometer or calutron for enriching uranium.[2] A slag of calcium and magnesium oxides forms too. Magnesium can be extracted by heating this slag mixture with silicon at about 1200 C. under reduced pressure. Magnesium evaporates and is condensed. The calcium silicate slag remaining can be broken up and used as aggregate in concrete or it can be processed to get calcium compounds and even pure calcium metal. Processing slag might involve sulfuric acid leaching, roasting with carbon and electrolysis in FFC cells.

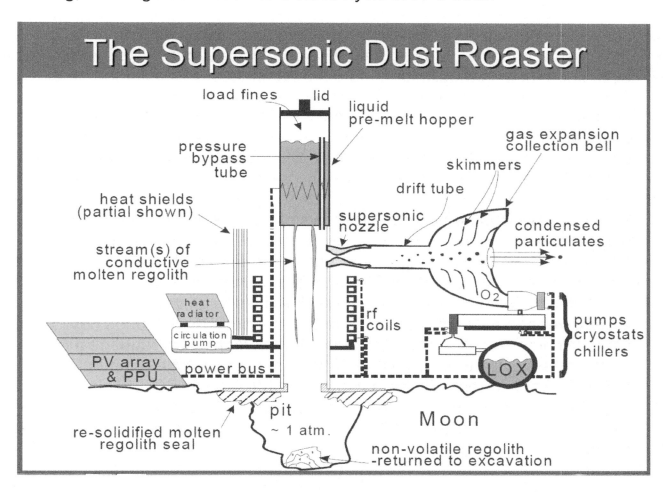

Fig. 2 Dr. Schubert's device for decomposing regolith with intense heat for

oxygen and other elements.

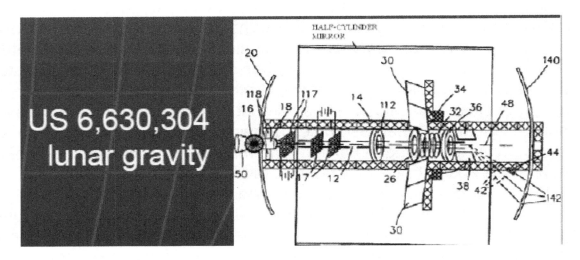

Fig. 3 An All-Isotope-Separator for operation in low lunar gravity.

Numerous processes for extracting oxygen and metals from lunar regolith have been proposed. Most of them use chemical reagents like hydrofluoric acid, fluorine, chlorine, lithium and other substances not common on the Moon. These chemicals will corrode things, leak and become contaminated over time. They will have to be replenished with imports from Earth at great cost. A process that doesn't require water and/or lots of corrosive and imported chemicals is desired. The Supersonic Dust Roaster and All Isotope Separator (SDR-AIS) fits the bill.

The SDR-AIS is based on complex laws of physics and is rather sophisticated. However, its operation is simple. Loads of regolith go in. Oxygen and metals come out. It is also much simpler than the hydrofluoric acid leach process studied by NASA.[3] This is important because in general, simpler systems are more reliable (less to go wrong) and less expensive than more complicated systems. The SDR-AIS does have to cope with intense corrosion from super-hot oxygen. This requires that parts of the device must be made of thorium oxide, a high temperature melting point ceramic. There is thorium on the Moon in KREEP laden regolith. This thorium can also be converted to uranium for nuclear reactors. Mining KREEP for thorium could be a strategic lunar industry someday.

1. $xMO \cdot SiO_2 + (4 + 2x)\, HF = xMF_2 + SiF_4\,(aq) + (2 + x)\, H_2O$
1′. $xMO \cdot SiO_2 + (5 + 2x)\, HF = xMF_2 + HSiF_5\,(aq) + (2 + x)\, H_2O$
2. $SiF_4\,(aq) + nH_2O = SiF_4\,(v) + nH_2O\,(v)$
2′. $HSiF_5\,(aq) + nH_2O = SiF_4\,(v) + HF\,(aq) + nH_2O\,(v)$
3. $(1 - y)\,[SiF_4\,(v) + 4H_2O = Si\,(OH)_4 + 4HF]$
3a. $(1 - y)\,[SiF_4\,(v) + 2H_2O = SiO_2 + 4HF]$
4. $(1 - y' - z)\,[xMF_2 + xH_2O = xMO + 2xHF]$
5. $y\,[SiF_4 + 4Na = Si + 4NaF]$
6. $y'\,[xMF_2 + 2xNa = xM + 2xNaF]$
7. $z\,[xMF_2 + xSiF_4\,(aq) = xMSiF_6\,(aq)]$
8. $z\,[xMSiF_4\,(aq) + xH_2O + \text{electrical energy} = (x/2)O_2 + xM + xH_2SiF_6]$
8a. $z\,[xMSiF_6\,(aq) + M'SO_3R^* = xM'SiF_6\,(aq) + xMSO_3R^*]$
9. $m\,NaF + mR^*OH = mNaOH + mR^*F$
9a. $m\,NaF + (m/2)\,Ca\,(OH)_2 = mNaOH + (m/w)\,CaF_2$
10. $m\,NaOH + \text{electrical energy} = mNa + (m/2)O_2 + (m/2)H_2O$
11. $(1 - y)\,[Si\,(OH)_4 = SiO_2 + 2H_2O]$

R^* = ion-exchange resin
$m = 4y + 2xy'$

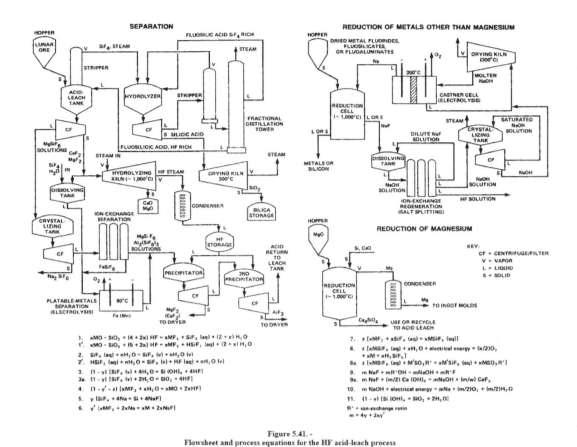

Figure 5.41. -
Flowsheet and process equations for the HF acid-leach process

Fig. 4 HF acid leach process from NASA's Advanced Automation for Space Missions study done in 1981.

The system pictured above consists of 34 component leaching tanks, distillation towers, centrifuges, precipitators, electrolysis cells, etc. There are 111 pipe connection points with at least one valve and control mechanism. Today's computers could easily control all this but the complexity equates with lower reliability and higher costs.

Simple Materials

Basaltic mare regolith can be excavated, pressed into iron forms and sintered with heat from solar or electrical furnaces, or melted at 1150 C. to 1350 C. and cast in iron molds to make numerous cast basalt items. It can also be melted and drawn into fibers. Highland regolith can be sintered or cast to make glassy products with a melting point of about 1500 C.

Meteoric iron fines can be magnetically extracted from large amounts of regolith just about anywhere on the Moon. After some grinding, screening and a second magnetic separation, 99% pure iron-nickel particles can be obtained.[4] This can be refined further with carbon monoxide to extract nickel. Another possibility is the use of a device similar to a mass spectrometer to separate iron, nickel, cobalt, gallium, germanium and platinum group metals from this meteoric material. It will also be possible to melt and cast the iron fines in sand molds. It should be possible to run these particles in 3D printers after sizing them to make iron-nickel items for low stress applications. It will also be possible to melt and cast the iron into rods, pack them in carbon powder, and get them red hot for a few days in solar or electrical furnaces to convert the iron into strong steel. So far, so good. Mining the Moon for these materials doesn't require any water, acids, halogens or other substances rare or practically non-existent on the Moon.

When water and sulfur are available it will be possible to make sulfuric acid on the Moon. This will be useful for extracting silica and making calcium sulfate. Silica or silicon dioxide is the main component of glass. Calcium sulfate is plaster of Paris. It is useful as is for making molds, sheet rock and it is a cement ingredient. It might also be decomposed with extreme heat in a solar furnace or reduced with carbon to get lime, CaO. Lime can be electrolyzed in FFC cells to get pure calcium metal.

Valuable Light Elements

Light elements like hydrogen, nitrogen and carbon are of great use. Hydrogen can be combined with oxygen to make water or it can be used as rocket fuel. It can also be reacted with carbon to make chemicals and plastics. Nitrogen can be used to make synthetic materials and it is needed for agriculture. Carbon is needed for agriculture and it is the backbone of organic chemicals and plastics.

Heating regolith to 700 C. will release hydrogen, helium and nitrogen. Carbon will react with oxygen in the regolith to form CO and CO_2 gases. Hydrogen will react with carbon to form methane and it will react with oxides to form water. These gases could be separated by fractional liquefication. At the University of Wisconsin in Madison, scientists have designed a machine that could dig up and heat regolith from a square kilometer of lunar surface to a depth of three meters in a year's time. They predict harvesting of substantial quantities of volatiles.[5]

Materials Harvested per Year in Tonnes

Element/Compound	Mass
water	109
nitrogen	16.5
CO_2	56
hydrogen	201
helium 4	102
methane (CH_4)	53
CO	63
helium 3	33 kg.

Enough hydrogen could be harvested to make 1800 metric tons of water when combined with oxygen extracted from regolith. This could support a population of several hundred persons on the Moon. The CO_2 molecules are very stable and require temperatures of 3000 C.+ to decompose at extremely low pressure.[6] The CO molecules have an even higher decomposition temperature and they can react with each other to form CO_2 and carbon.[7] It will require less energy to react these carbon oxides with hydrogen to make methane which can be decomposed at 900 C. to get pure carbon and recover hydrogen. The total amount of carbon from the masses of CO, CO_2 and CH_4 above will be 82 tons at 100% recovery. That's enough to make lots of steel and some plastics too. Chances are less carbon than that will be obtained, but the CO and CO_2 remaining will have uses.

Polar ices may also serve as a source of water and thus hydrogen and oxygen for fuel cell reactants and rocket propellants. LCROSS data showed that the ice contains ammonia (NH_3), methane (CH_4), carbon monoxide and carbon dioxide. The CO_2 will be needed for plant growth in hydroponic farms. Hydrogen and CO can be combined to make many different organic chemicals. Ammonia can provide nitrogen for atmospheres and fertilizer.

Resources for the Future

Excavators, transports, solar power plants, regolith refining equipment, manufacturing machines, vehicles, inflatable habitat, superconducting wire for the mass driver launcher and robots will be landed on the Moon. Some pieces of equipment will be made partly on the Moon. Eventually all things including water and food will be produced on the Moon.

Lots of cargo will be required to do this job. It will be necessary to figure out how to make all this on the Moon from an initial stock of devices or a "lunar industrial seed" that might have a mass of several hundred to several thousand tons. Energy requirements and times for each step of the process must be calculated; a job for chemical and industrial engineers. The economics of all processes must be determined by doing research on the ground in vacuum chambers that simulate the lunar environment, at lunar analog research bases and at a Lunar Industrial Research Park on the Moon where hard facts are determined.

Naturally, many solar panels will be needed to power this equipment. The 3D printers, casting foundries and machine shops where we replicate this regolith refinery equipment will not be limited to the expansion of the refinery. They will also use lunar materials to crank out all the other items needed for life in space including bathroom and kitchen fixtures, plumbing systems, everyday items like dishes and bottles, robot parts, vehicle parts and complete vehicles, excavator parts and complete excavators, spacecraft and more 3D printers and machine tools.

At some point in time, growth of the lunar mining, refining and manufacturing complex will become exponential. The first base will produce enough stuff to build a second base, then a third and fourth base, then eight bases, sixteen bases, etc. We will need dirt roads and eventually railways to connect the bases. Sub-orbital rockets could provide high speed "air travel" across the Moon.

A vast amount of solar power generation and distribution infrastructure will also be built. Along the equator, two other solar power stations in addition to the solar panels at the base could be built 90 to 120 degrees (1700 to 2260 miles) east and west of the main base. Superconducting coils will be imported for the mass driver lunar launcher, but superconductors will not be practical for the long distance power lines. Calcium is actually a better conductor than copper, but little is known about calcium metallurgy.[8] Calcium wires are not used on Earth because it reacts with moisture and can ignite spontaneously in air. This won't be a problem in the vacuum. It might be possible to use calcium cables clad with aluminum. Electrical conductivity depends on the choice of material. It also depends on wire thickness, length and temperature. Thicker wires are more conductive while longer wires present more resistance especially at higher temperatures. It might be possible to transmit high voltage AC power across the Moon through extra thick cables that would be too heavy on Earth. The cables could be shielded from the extreme heat of lunar day with foil or sheet metal.

A constant source of electrical power will make it possible to illuminate crops throughout the night and provide heat for equipment. It might even be possible to keep mining and launching materials during nightspan with enough energy. Nuclear power is also possible. Radioisotope heating units each containing a few grams of nuclear material might be essential for the nightspan survival of equipment, especially in the early stages of building a mining base. Dr. Peter Schubert and his associates at Purdue University, Indiana, have designed a system for extracting thorium from KREEP (a kind of regolith enriched in potassium, rare earth elements and phosphorus) and transmuting it to U233 for reactor fuel. Thorium is placed in a vessel with an outer layer of beryllium that emits neutrons when struck by abundant space gamma rays. An inner layer of graphite moderates the neutrons so that they are absorbed by the thorium which then decays via protactinium to uranium. It is predicted that mining and extraction equipment, a beryllium-graphite transmutation vessel, a reactor and a helium filled turbogenerator system will only weigh about 54 metric tons. This system could generate 2 MWe for several years. No radioactive materials would have to be transported through Earth's atmosphere by rockets that sometimes explode. This is a very important development.

Resources of Mars

Notes on Martian Geology

Mars is much different than the Moon. The gravity is higher at about 3/8s that of Earth versus $1/6^{th}$ for the Moon. It has a thin atmosphere and it is rather certain that there was once liquid water on Mars when the atmosphere was thicker and the surface was warmer. Unlike the Moon, Mars has sedimentary rocks like sandstone, clays, hematite and sulfates including gypsum. There appear to be numerous chloride deposits as well as perchlorates in the regolith. Olivine, pyroxene and feldspar are present in basalt, a resource of great importance on Mars as well as the Moon. Martian regolith contains oxygen, silicon, iron, aluminum, magnesium, calcium, sodium and smaller amounts of titanium, chromium, manganese, sulfur, potassium and phosphorus. Traces of zinc and copper exist.[9] Given the existence of hydrological processes, some of these elements might be concentrated into rock deposits that could be classified as ores. More exploration, perhaps by humans, is called for. Whereas lunar mining is limited to basaltic mare regolith and anorthositic highland regolith, Mars mining might be done at sites rich in a particular element or small group of elements. A number of mine sites could be linked to a central base by dirt roads and eventually railways. This could be very efficient.

Ices

At the Martian north polar cap in the summertime, the frozen CO_2 sublimates away and leaves water ice. At the south pole in the summer, some CO_2 remains over the water ice. It is also believed that ice exists beneath about a third of the Martian surface. These ices could be sources of water, hydrogen, oxygen and carbon.

Atmosphere

The atmosphere of Mars is composed mainly of carbon dioxide (95%) with nitrogen (2.7%), argon (1.6%), oxygen (0.13%), carbon monoxide (0.08%), and minor levels of water, nitrogen oxide, neon, hydrogen, deuterium, krypton, and xenon. It is only 1% as dense as Earth's atmosphere. Compressors with intakes the size of jet engines could pump down the low pressure gases and separate them with membranes, pressure swing absorption and/or fractional liquefication at low temperatures. Nitrogen could be used for breathing gas mixtures. It could also be combined with hydrogen to make ammonia for fertilizer. Argon might be used as a welding shield gas. The CO_2 could be used to sustain crops and it could be reacted with hydrogen in a Sabatier reactor to make methane. A Sabatier reactor is basically just a tube containing a nickel catalyst. It could also be reacted with hydrogen to make water, carbon monoxide and hydrogen.[10]

$H_2 + CO_2 \rightarrow H_2O + CO$ Reverse Water Gas Shift reaction Fe-Cr catalyst
$3H_2 + CO_2 \rightarrow H_2O + CO + 2H_2$

Water, of course, is useful as is for life support, but it can also be electrolyzed to hydrogen and oxygen. Hydrogen and carbon monoxide together are known as synthesis gas. In various proportions, temperatures, pressures and with the right catalysts almost any organic chemical can be made from this mixture. Methanol, acetic acid, formaldehyde, ethane, methane, ethylene, propylene and other chemicals for making plastics, synthetic fibers, and more could all be produced on Mars from plentiful local resources of water and CO_2. On Mars, it would be possible to mine enough water ice, dry ice and atmospheric CO_2 to make chemicals for large settlements of several thousand to perhaps a million people. This wouldn't be as easy as refining oil on Earth, but it would allow more synthetic materials for Martians than is possible on the Moon. Reducing by using substitutes of metal, glass and basalt, reusing and recycling of all plastics, rubber, silicones, lubricating oil, etc. would be essential.

Extraction

According to Dr. Peter Schubert, his Super-sonic Dust Roaster might work in the thin atmosphere of Mars, but the All Isotope Separator must have vacuum. Terrestrial processes like carbon reduction of metal oxide ores might be adapted for use on Mars. Dr. Geoffrey A. Landis has worked out a process for extracting metals from lunar regolith that might be adapted to work on Mars.[11] He proposes shipping potassium fluoride salts to the Moon. Since KF salt is stable and non-cryogenic it could be shipped to Mars in plastic containers as easily as it could be shipped to the Moon. The KF salt is electrolyzed to get fluorine gas to which the regolith is subjected. Silicon tetrafluoride and titanium tetrafluoride gases evolve. Other volatile compounds including water from ice could be driven out of the regolith by roasting before treatment with fluorine. The SiF_4 and TiF_4 are then reduced with potassium to get silicon and titanium. It might be preferable to decompose SiF_4 directly with heat to get silicon of higher purity. Fluorides of iron, aluminum, magnesium and calcium form. Iron and aluminum fluorides can be reduced with potassium and the metals separated from the salt by melting. Aluminum might be boiled away from the iron under low pressure. Other methods of separating these two metals also exist. Some iron-aluminides might form that have industrial uses. Magnesium and calcium fluorides cannot be reduced with potassium. Potassium could be oxidized and then reacted with these salts. A substitution reaction takes place and CaO and MgO form along with KF. The KF is then electrolyzed to get fluorine and potassium to repeat the process with more regolith.

Silicothermic reduction of magnesium ore is the primary method of magnesium production on Earth today. The mixture of CaO and MgO could be mixed with pulverized silicon and heated to 1200 C. under low pressure. Magnesium will evaporate and can be condensed. The remaining slag of $CaSiO_3$ could be broken up as is and used as cement aggregate or it could be processed further. It could be leached with sulfuric acid made from local sources of water and sulfur with an imported vanadium pentoxide catalyst to get SiO_2 and $CaSO_4$. These could be separated electrostatically perhaps and the silica can be used to make glass while the calcium sulfate can be used for plaster and molds. The $CaSO_4$ might also be decomposed with heat or reduced with carbon to get lime (CaO), CO and SO_2 for reconstituting the sulfuric acid. The lime could be used to make mortar and cement or it could be electrolyzed in FFC cells to get calcium metal and oxygen.

Dr. Landis has also proposed a lunar regolith process involving the reduction of all metals in the regolith with pure calcium metal. The metals could be separated by vacuum distillation. Could low pressure distillation on Mars be done? The calcium oxide that forms is recycled to calcium metal by electrolysis of the lime in FFC cells.[12]

Carbon

Mars has plenty of accessible carbon, unlike the Moon that only has traces in the form of solar wind implanted volatiles and polar ices. Since carbon oxides, CO and CO_2, require high temperatures to decompose, it is "easier" to react these compounds with hydrogen to make methane and decompose the methane to elemental carbon and hydrogen (which can be recycled) at about 900 C. This pure carbon has many uses. It can be burned to make CO and CO_2 as needed. It can be used to convert iron to steel and it can be reacted with lime at high temperatures in a solar or electric arc furnace to make calcium carbide. When calcium carbide reacts with water it forms acetylene gas which can be passed through a red hot iron tube at about 600 C. to make benzene, a chemical with a great many uses. More about that later. Activated carbon can be used to filter air and water. Carbon fibers are very strong and can reinforce other materials. Chances are that basalt fibers which can be stronger than steel and glass fibers will be used more often to make cables for pre-stressing structures.

Copper and Zinc

Traces of copper and zinc have been detected in the regolith of Mars. Dr. Robert Zubrin has suggested that given the presence of these elements, there may be concentrations or ore bodies of hydrological origin on Mars. Pure aluminum is not a particularly strong metal. The best alloys, like 2000 series, are made with copper and 7000 series are made with zinc. The 7000 series can be precipitation hardened to the highest strengths of any aluminum alloy. Most 7000 series alloys include magnesium and copper as well. On the Moon, there is really nothing to alloy aluminum with besides silicon, magnesium and manganese. In low lunar gravity it might be possible to get by with these "second best" alloys.

Copper is also a much better conductor than aluminum. Copper is the preferred electrical conductor for all kinds of things even though aluminum is used for long distance power cables due to its lighter weight. Copper is used in generators, transformers, household wiring, telecommunication cables, electronics, heat sinks, heat exchangers, magnetrons in microwave ovens and other things. There are good reasons that the cables connected to your computer are made of copper instead of aluminum! It makes electric motors more efficient. Lunans should welcome copper to replace aluminum electric motor coils. On Earth, electric motors account for 43% to 46% of all electric power consumption and 69% of all the power used by industry.[13] Lunans and free space settlers will be just as reliant on electric motors if not more, since vehicles including trains and excavators will all be propelled by electric motors instead of internal combustion engines. Electric motors will be needed to drive water and sewage pumps, refrigerators and heavy cryogenic equipment, compressors, machine tools, hand power tools, ventilation and air filtration fans, rolling mills, hydraulic pumps for extruders and other machines, forced convection fans in weightless ovens, cooling fans, jackscrews for steering rocket motors, elevators, spin matching cars and centrifuges in spaceships, electric knives, kitchen equipment like mixers and blenders, conveyor belts, robots, cranes, etc. The electric motor may be as great an invention as the light bulb! Copper is even used for pigments, plumbing, architecture, jewelry and cookware. And it's antibacterial and antimicrobial. Lunans and free space dwellers might welcome copper and zinc from Mars for stronger aluminum alloys, electric motors, etc.

Chlorine

At least 640 chloride deposits have been detected on Mars and the regolith contains perchlorates at about 0.5%.[14] That chlorine must be washed out of the regolith before any farming in it on Mars can be done. Chlorine is a very useful element. Chlorine is needed to make methyl chloride used in silicone polymer synthesis. It is needed to make salt when combined with sodium. Potassium can also be combined with chlorine to make potassium chloride which some people use as a salt substitute. Chlorine is needed to make PVC, many other plastics and silane rocket fuel. It can be used to treat water, make bleach and dry cleaning fluid-carbon tetrachloride. With growing populations on the Moon and in free space settlements the demand for these substances may become worth supplying to earn money. Since it takes less energy to travel from Mars to the Moon than from Earth to the Moon, entrepreneurs on the Moon and in Earth orbital space might buy their chlorine from Mars someday, presuming that would be cheaper.

Asteroid Resources

Quick Facts

There are over a million known asteroids. Most are found in the Main Belt between Mars and Jupiter. Scientists estimate that there are 1.1 million to 1.9 million asteroids over 1 km in diameter in the belt and many more smaller ones.[15] The Jupiter Trojans may be as numerous as the asteroids of the Main Belt. There are over 10,000 asteroids that pass near Earth and some even cross Earth's orbit. These are called Near Earth Asteroids (NEAs). These NEAs may contain elements valuable for industry on the Moon and in Earth orbital space. Despite their huge numbers, it is believed that the mass of the main belt asteroids is only 3% of that of the Moon, with the four largest asteroids containing 62% of that mass.[16]

There are three classifications of asteroids:

C-type (chondrite)

These dark objects consist of clay and silicate rocks and often contain carbon and water. About 75% of all asteroids are of this type. They contain up to 3% carbon in the form of graphite, carbonates and organic compounds including amino acids. In addition, they contain water and minerals that have been modified by the effects of water. CI chondrites contain up to 22% water and organic matter in the form of Polycyclic Aromatic Hydrocarbons (PAHs) and amino acids.[17] Some C-type asteroids contain phosphorus and other fertilizer elements.[18] This kind of asteroid is most interesting as a source of light elements for the Moon, Earth orbital and solar orbital space ("free space") settlements.

There are many NEAs that pass near Earth and it takes less energy to reach many of them from Earth orbit than it does to reach the Moon; however, launch windows to and from these asteroids are years apart. If the hydrogen, carbon and nitrogen resources of C-type NEAs are to be obtained the job will probably be done by artificially intelligent robots. It might be possible for robotic mining ships to extract the water and organics for return to Earth orbital space and leave the depleted rock behind. Water might be used for rocket fuel, but it may be more economical to use the depleted rock as reaction mass for mass driver engines or ablation propulsion systems.

S-type (stony)

These asteroids are made mostly of silicate minerals and nickel-iron. They are rich in iron-magnesium silicates which of course contain large amounts of silicon and oxygen along with lesser amounts of aluminum and calcium bearing silicates.

M-type (metallic)

Only about 8% of all asteroids are M-type. The metallic asteroids are about 80% iron and 20% nickel, iridium, palladium, platinum, gold, magnesium and other precious metals such as osmium, ruthenium and rhodium.[19] With carbon from C-type asteroids and nickel-iron from M-type asteroids, it may be possible to make steel for large rotating space settlements. The presence of precious metals could make mining this kind of asteroid very lucrative. Since these asteroids were probably once molten and have long since solidified, it might be necessary for robotic miners to cut them up with high energy lasers or electron beams.

Basalt

Description

Basalt is a kind of fine grained rock formed of hardened lava. It is made mostly of iron-magnesium silicates like olivines and pyroxenes with some feldspar. The seas of the Moon are filled with pulverized basalt after eons of meteoric bombardment and there is basalt on Mars on the slopes of the great volcanoes. Basalt can be mined, melted and cast into iron molds to make various small and medium sized things. Larger items like kitchen and bathroom fixtures can be cast in expendable sand molds. Molten basalt can be extruded through bushings and allowed to cool to make fibers that can be stronger than steel; however, cast basalt is like cement. It is strong in compression (78,000 psi) and weak in tension (5,100 psi). Pressurized structures made of basalt would demand very thick walls and be rather massive. Given the ease of mining basalt, especially on the Moon, and the possibility of 3D printing of basalt structures, this material is very attractive. Basalt powder can also be pressed into iron forms and sintered. Iron can be obtained on the Moon and Mars in various ways and iron molds and forms for casting and sintering basalt could be made by 3D printing.

It resists up to 98% sulfuric acid solutions, 30% NaOH (caustic, lye), is virtually impervious to water and organic chemicals like methanol and acetone and it is non-toxic. It will be attacked by halogens, HCl and HF acid.

Basalt could be a very important base material. It is harder than steel and abrasion resistant, so it will resist wear by sharp regolith particles. However, it is brittle. Basalt parts can be heat treated by heating them up in furnaces and letting them cool slowly and recrystallize. This is called annealing. Annealing softens metals and lets them be worked more easily, but it appears to strengthen basalt. Heating up basalt parts and plunging them in oil or water would probably make them crack instead of harden and strengthen them.

Uses for basalt include: [20]

Cast basalt

machine base supports (lathes, milling machines), furnace lining for resources extraction operations, large tool beds, crusher jaws, pipes and conduits, conveyor material (pneumatic, hydraulic, sliding), linings for ball, tube or pug mills, flue ducts, ventilators, cyclers, drains, mixers, tanks, electrolyzers, and mineral dressing equipment, tiles and bricks, sidings, expendable ablative hull material (possibly composited with spun basalt), track rails, "railroad" ties, pylons, heavy duty containers for "agricultural" use, radar dish or mirror frames, thermal rods or heat pipes housings, supports and backing for solar collectors

Sintered basalt

nozzles, tubing, wire-drawing dies, ball bearings, wheels, low torque fasteners, studs, furniture and utensils, low load axles, scientific equipment, frames and yokes, light tools, light duty containers and flasks for laboratory use, pump housings, filters/partial plugs

Spun basalt (fibers)

cloth and bedding, resilient shock absorbing pads, acoustic insulation, thermal insulation, insulator for prevention of cold welding of metals, filler in sintered "soil" cement, fine springs, packing material, strainers or filters for industrial or agricultural use, electrical insulation, ropes for cables (with coatings)

More everyday items that could be made of cast, sintered or fiber basalt include plates, dishes, mugs, tea cups, bowls, tea and coffee pots, serving trays, pitchers, decanters, counter tops, kitchen sinks, table tops, table legs, stools, chairs, bars, shelves, bottles, jugs, hand basins, toilets, bath tubs, shower stalls, bidets, planting containers, flower pots, vases, lamps, water pipes and sewer pipes, ash trays, paper weights, candle sticks, aquaculture tanks, floor, ceiling and wall tiles, bricks, blocks, towel racks, clothes racks, shower curtain racks, shower curtain rings, shower curtains from basalt fiber, drapes, cushions of woven fiber stuffed with fiber, mattresses, rugs, statuary, doors, handles and knobs for doors and drawers, picture frames and certainly other things. Small items could be cast or sintered in 3D printed iron molds while large items like toilets and aquaculture tanks could be cast in expendable sand molds bound with sodium silicate.

There isn't any clay on the Moon and very little with which to make resin for binding sand molds, besides wet sand would dry out rapidly in the vacuum. There is plenty of sodium oxide and silicon dioxide to make sodium silicate which can be dissolved in water, mixed with sand inside pressurized habitat, of course, then dried out with microwaves to make sand molds into which molten metals, basalt or glass are poured into outside in the vacuum. Mars does have clays, so it might be possible to bind sand molds with clay on Mars.

Basalt or other forms of regolith could be melted and extruded to print large structures. Walls would have to be about ten inches thick to hold pressure. These would be heavy stationary permanent structures. More portable temporary structures could be made of metal plates.

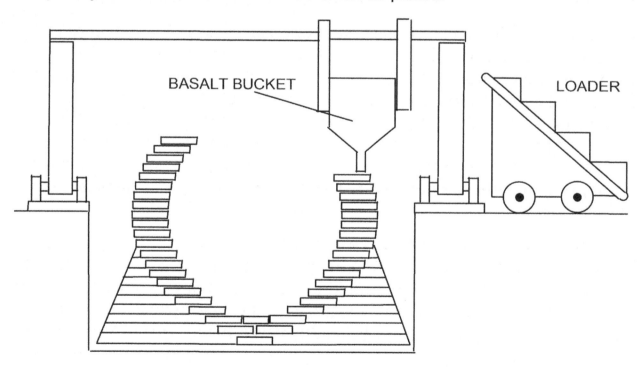

Fig. 5 Cross sectional diagram of machine printing cylindrical habitat with extruded molten basalt.

Iron and Steel

Iron and steel are made on Earth with huge blast furnaces filled with burning coke (purified coal) that use huge blasts of air and release tons of CO_2. Obviously, this won't work in space. There isn't enough carbon and there isn't enough air, although oxygen could be made. The cast iron that comes from blast furnaces contains about 3.5% carbon. Molten cast iron is subjected to a blast of oxygen in a basic oxygen furnace to burn out some of the carbon and get it down to 0.05% to 2% carbon. Then it is called steel. Steel is stronger and less brittle than cast iron. It can be tailored to almost any application by adjusting carbon content, alloying with nickel, chromium, manganese and other elements, and by heat treating. It is a very versatile metal. In space, we will need some steel, although we won't be able to have the enormous quantities that we can have on Earth.

On the Moon it should be possible to produce pure iron with Super-sonic Dust Roasters and All Isotope Separators. Pure iron has properties similar to that of wrought iron-about 40,000 psi compressive and tensile strength. It can be used for ornate works, nails (in aerated auto-claved concrete), hinges, pins, pots, pans, rails, handles, rods, furniture, etc. Wrought iron was used for steam train rails before the now obsolete Bessemer Process made large amounts of cheap steel available in the 19th century. In the low gravity and rust free vacuum of the Moon pure iron might be sufficient for railway tracks.

On Mars, iron might be extracted with fluorine. It might also be possible to separate hematite, an iron bearing mineral, and smelt it in Direct Reduced Iron furnaces. These furnaces would use electric heat and mixtures of hydrogen from water and CO by electrolysis of CO_2 to reduce hematite to pig iron. Flux from gypsum or carbonates which *might* exist of Mars would be used to absorb the silica from the hematite. To convert the pig iron to steel would require oxygen from water and a basic oxygen furnace. The steam and CO_2 generated by the DRI Furnaces might be recycled and broken back down into hydrogen and carbon monoxide. Electrolysis is one way to convert CO_2 to CO. It might also be possible to react CO_2 with hydrogen to make methane, water and some CO. The methane could be partially combusted to make more CO.

Steel making on the Moon or in free space will involve pure iron extraction. Instead of burning carbon out of cast or pig iron, carbon will be added to the iron with the ancient crucible steel process. This is called carburization. Pure iron will be cast into rods or bars, packed in carbon and heated to red heat in electric furnaces for up to a week. The iron will absorb carbon and become steel. Since the outer layers of the metal bars will have more carbon in them than the inner layers, it will be necessary to melt the metal in an electric furnace to homogenize it. Some calcium aluminate flux made by roasting anorthosite at 2000 C. or hotter could be added to the molten steel to remove impurities. The steel could then be sand cast and machined to make heavy things like rolling mills. Slabs of steel could be rolled to plates, sheets or rails. It could be drawn into wires or powdered and fed into 3D printers to make various parts.

Steel is needed for threaded pipes, fittings, nuts, bolts and screws. Fortunately, the required mass of these will not be too large. Steel is needed in moderate quantities for threaded parts, nuts, bolts, ball bearings, roller bearings, hand tools, power tools, cutting tools (cemented carbides might also be used) drill bits (cobalt steel), machines like lathes, grinders, milling machines, extruders (for chambers and rams), gears, drive shafts, axles (titanium might suffice for that), razors and good knives. Strong maraging steel contains almost no carbon but does require cobalt (from meteoric iron-nickel fines) and molybdenum and can be used for things like rocket motor casings but it won't take a good edge for blades and knives. Nickel, chromium and manganese exist on the Moon for steel alloys like stainless steel. Steel metallurgy, like chemistry, is a very mature science. Steel's only major weakness is that it rusts. That will not be a problem in the lunar vacuum or outer space. There isn't enough oxygen or water vapor on Mars to rust steel either. Steel can be easily recycled by melting in an electric arc or solar furnace and re-casting.

Steel can be made harder, stronger and more durable by heat treating. Parts are heated to temperatures above the austenitic transition or recrystallization temperature but not as high as the melting point of the metal. After some time at this heat the parts are quenched with water or oil. This hardens the metal. It is then heated up again, but not quite as hot as before, and allowed to cool slowly. This is called tempering and it reduces some of the hardness but makes the steel less brittle. Water and oil quenching would have to be done in pressurized modules to prevent evaporation of the oil or water which would flash into vapor outside in the vacuum. Large inflatable habitat with concrete floors and powerful air conditioning systems might be needed. Water can be produced on the Moon or Mars and steam from the quenching could be recaptured from the air with dehumidifiers. Mineral oil is usually used for oil quenching, but this substance is not to be had in space. Vegetable oils or silicone oils might be used instead.

Different kinds of steel with various carbon contents and alloying ingredients require different temperatures, times at heat, and different quenching mediums be they water, oil or molten salts. This is rather complicated but the steel industry has researched heat treatment extensively and isothermal diagrams for the processes have been made.

Steel can also be heat treated to make it softer and easier to work with by machining it or deforming it. It is heated then cooled very slowly. This is called annealing. After the annealed parts are shaped they can be hardened and strengthened by heating and rapid quenching. Parts can be annealed in a furnace where temperatures are gradually reduced. This requires energy. It is also possible to bury a hot part in insulating vermiculites that trap the heat and allow the part to cool slowly. Lunar regolith is an excellent thermal insulator, therefore it may be possible to cover hot parts with loose regolith to anneal them.

Steel parts can be heated with flames, electric induction heaters or molten salt baths. Gas flames are not likely on the Moon, Mars or space manufacturing stations. Not only does natural gas not exist there, it would release a lot of CO_2 into the air. Hydrogen flames that emit only easily recovered non-toxic water vapor might be used. Induction heating uses a radio frequency coil to heat metal parts. Salt baths heated by the resistance of an electric current passed through the molten salt might be useful. Heating is rapid because it occurs by conduction. Parts can also be quenched in low temperature salt baths. Rapid quenching in water or oil can lead to cracking and defects in the metal. Quenching in salt allows a slower and more controlled cooling.

Heat Treatment Salt Bath Compositions

	Composition	Melting Point	Work Temperature Range
A	NaOH 75% KOH 19% H_2O 6%	140°C.	160-280°C.
B	KOH 50-60% NaOH 40-50%		300-400°C.
C	KNO_3 100%	337°C.	350-500°C.
D	KNO_3 50-60% $NaNO_2$ 40-50%	135°C.	160-550°C.
E	$NaNO_3$ 50-60% $NaNO_2$ 40-50%	145°C.	150-500°C.
F	KNO_3 50-60% $NaNO_3$ 40-50%	225°C.	260-600°C.
G	$NaNO_3$ 100%	370°C.	400-600°C.
H	NaCl 10-15% KCl 20-30% $BaCl_2$ 40-50% $CaCl_2$ 15-20%	400°C.	500-800°C.
I	$NaCO_3$ 45-55% KCl 45-55%	450°C.	550-900°C.
J	$BaCl_2$ 50% KCl 30% NaCl 20%	540°C.	570-900°C.
K	$BaCl_2$ 70-96% NaCl 4-30%	600-800°C.	700-1250°C.

Sodium (Na), potassium (K), and calcium (Ca) can be produced on the Moon or Mars. Barium (Ba) would have to be imported from Earth. Chlorine (Cl) is available in Martian perchlorates and lunar appatite by sulfuric acid leaching, and some might be imported. Hydroxides (OH) can be made by direct reaction of sodium or potassium with water, but this reaction is rather violent. Castner-Kellner cells, water and NaCl can be used to make NaOH. Carbonates (CO_3) might be made by reaction with carbon dioxide and nitrates (NO_2 and NO_3) would require nitric acid made from ammonia from lunar polar ice or by reacting hydrogen with nitrogen.

Non-Ferrous Metals

The most abundant non-ferrous metals on the Moon, excluding calcium, are aluminum, magnesium and titanium. There are smaller amounts of chromium and manganese. These will be needed for spacecraft, ground vehicles and solar power satellites because of their light weight and high strength. Magnesium is not particularly strong, but it can be used for low stress parts like sheet metal reflectors that concentrate solar energy onto photovoltaic modules at surface bases and on solar power satellites. Aluminum would be the primary structural material for powersat trusses and frameworks with titanium parts at hard points. It's also possible that power satellite frames could be made of glass fiber reinforced glass matrix or silica fiber reinforced basalt matrix composites. Aluminum composes about 7% of the lunar regolith, magnesium 6% and titanium about 3% although titanium content varies depending on location. Silicon dioxide composes about 40% of the regolith and mare regolith is 100% basalt. If glass or basalt based composites can be used for powersat construction, the mined regolith can be used much more efficiently. Aluminum and magnesium could be used for reflectors. Titanium might still be used for hard points.

Spacecraft and ground vehicles could have titanium frames and aluminum skins like jet fighters. Magnesium might be used for low stress parts and lightweight wheels. It could also be used to alloy aluminum and make it stronger. Conversely, aluminum can be added to magnesium to make it stronger. Alloys might also be made with silicon and manganese. There isn't enough copper and zinc on the Moon to make the best aluminum and magnesium alloys, but there might be on Mars. The most popular titanium alloy contains 6% aluminum and 4% vanadium. Vanadium is present in only parts per million in the lunar regolith. As for its presence on Mars, this is unknown. Silicon, iron or chromium might substitute for vanadium in titanium alloys, but these will be a bit heavier. Titanium aluminides which are very hard and corrosion resistant might also be produced.

Iron composes about 14% of the lunar regolith and it is present in hematite and regolith on Mars. Steel requires carbon which is abundant on Mars but not on the Moon. Fortunately, a small amount of carbon can make a large quantity of steel. Iron and steel will find many uses where lightweight is not so important. It would be foolish to ignore the use of iron and steel and try to make everything out of aluminum, magnesium and titanium. Spacecraft and powersats must be lightweight, but space stations and surface modules could be made of steel. Iron might also be powdered and mixed with silane for rocket fuel. Heavy excavating equipment might be made of steel. It could also be made of titanium. Heavy extruder machines and rolling mills would be made of steel. Railroad tracks might be made of pure iron or mild steel to conserve carbon. Railroad cars would probably be made with aluminum, magnesium and titanium.

Calcium is interesting because it is a better electrical conductor than copper. However, it reacts with moisture and oxygen and can spontaneously ignite in air. In the vacuum, this won't be a problem. Calcium is also useful in its oxide form for mortar and cement. Along with sodium oxide, calcium oxide can be used to lower the melting point of glass.

Aluminum is easy to extrude into rods, bars, rails and parts with complex cross sections. It is also easy to roll into plate, sheets, foils and other things like beams and pipes. Magnesium lacks ductility and is hard to shape by deformation, but it can be heated up to make it softer and hot rolled or extruded. Titanium is very hard to roll or extrude, but this can be done with hot titanium. Aluminum and magnesium melt at 660° C. and 600° C. respectively. They could easily be cast in molds made of lunar regolith bound with sodium silicate dried out with microwaves. Iron and steel casting would demand real silica sand that melts at 1700° C. since they melt at 1200° C. to 1500° C. and mare regolith melts at 1250° C. Highland regolith melts at about 1500° C. Fortunately, silica can easily be produced by sulfuric acid leaching of regolith. Casting titanium will require imported zirconium oxide and yttrium oxide sands and electron beam furnaces because of its high melting point and reactivity. Most titanium will either be shaped by CNC machines or powdered and 3D printed with electron beam sintering machines.

Pure aluminum will be the primary material for power cables, electric wires, transformer windings and electric motor coils. The aluminum must be pure because alloys have more resistance. Aluminum clad with iron might be used for third rails for railroads. Aluminum bearing minerals, mostly anorthosite, $CaAl_2Si_2O_8$, are abundant in highland soils like those in the polar areas. Magnesium and titanium, along with iron, are more abundant in mare regolith. Since NASA plans to go to the polar regions to mine for ice, the use of aluminum is most important. Someday, private industry will locate a mass driver lunar launcher and mining base on the equator at 33.1 degrees East. Nearby mare regolith and highland regolith will be tapped for a whole suite of metals and other materials like cast basalt and glass.

The mass driver will probably launch raw regolith into space where it is separated into its component elements with devices resembling mass spectrometers or calutrons. Aluminum, magnesium and titanium compose only 16% of the regolith by mass. It might make more sense to process the metals out on the Moon and launch the metals needed for powersat construction into space and leave the rest in slag heaps on the Moon. On the other hand, if glass or basalt based composites are possible, raw regolith might be the best thing. All that oxygen (40% of the regolith) resulting from the smelting of metals from Moon dust and all the excess silicon, iron and calcium might find other purposes. Iron could be converted to steel and used for space stations. It might also be mixed with silane made from silicon and hydrogen piggybacked on rockets into space and used for rocket fuel. Silicon powder and calcium also burn in pure oxygen, and there will be more than enough oxygen for rockets if raw regolith is launched into space and processed there. Solar powersat construction might require non-ferrous metals mostly, but the other elements can be put to good use too. A thriving space travel industry could buy up all the oxygen, iron, calcium and silicon in GEO slag heaps where the powersat construction is going on and use it for rocket propellant and space hotel construction.

Chromium and manganese exist on the Moon in small but significant amounts. Chromium can be used to make stainless steel and manganese can make 3000 series aluminum alloys. Silicon is not a metal but a semi-metal. It can also be used to alloy aluminum by itself and in combination with magnesium.

Cement

Cement Defined

Portland cement is more than just a mixture of lime, CaO, sand and some gypsum (calcium sulfate). Plain mortar for bricks is made by mixing sand with slaked lime ($Ca(OH)_2$). This material will absorb CO_2 from the air and become harder. A better mortar is made by mixing Portland cement with sand. Cement is composed of a mixture of calcium silicates, mostly Ca_2SiO_4, Ca_3SiO_5, and calcium aluminate, $Ca_3Al_2O_6$. The calcium aluminate hydrolyzes when mixed with water and forms calcium hydroxide and aluminum hydroxide. The calcium silicates react with the hydroxides and form intermeshed crystals of calcium aluminosilicates.[21]

Concrete is made by mixing cement, sand and crushed rock or gravel with water. The sand and gravel are called aggregate and various other things like ash from coal plants and crushed glass have been used. Less cement is needed for a construction job when using concrete.

Making Lunar Cement & Concrete

On Earth limestone and clay are mixed together and heated to 1500 C. to get clinker. The limestone breaks down into lime and CO_2. The clay, which is basically just feldspar or plagioclase like the Highland regolith, reacts with the lime to make the mixture of calcium silicates and calcium aluminate called Portland cement.

On the Moon we will get a mixture of silica, SiO_2, and calcium sulfate, $CaSO_4$, after leaching magnetically beneficiated regolith that has had the iron and ilmenite ($FeTiO_3$ which also contains the titanium) removed, with sulfuric acid to extract aluminum sulfate and magnesium sulfate and some trace metals. Sulfur is fairly abundant in regolith at 500 ppm or more and could be obtained during volatile harvesting. Most of the sulfur and sulfuric acid will be recycled. The sulfates will be dewatered and roasted at 1000 C. or hotter to form oxides and gaseous SO_2 and SO_3 which can be reacted with water to reform sulfuric acid. The $CaSO_4$ can be calcined, or heated to high temperatures (~1500 C.) in solar furnaces, or reduced with carbon, to get lime, CaO. This can be mixed with aluminous Highland regolith in the right proportions and heated in solar furnaces to make small glassy marbles called "clinker" which are then ground in a ball mill. This powder is then mixed with $CaSO_4$ about 5% and ground some more to make cement.

Acid leaching puts precious water at risk and requires complex apparatus to leach and recycle everything, but it's the only way to get $CaSO_4$ on the Moon. Calcining this to get lime might not be the best way to make the actual cement. Anorthite, $CaAl_2Si_2O_8$, which composes 75% to 98% of highland regolith based on analysis of Apollo samples can be roasted at 2000 C. in the vacuum to decompose the mineral and drive off the SiO_2 component leaving calcium aluminate, $CaAl_2O_4$, behind.[22] Calcium aluminate makes good cement. Calcium sulfate is added to retard setting time.

On the Moon, water will come from polar ice, hydrogen from volatile harvesting combined with oxygen, and imported hydrogen combined with lunar oxygen. Since water is only 1/9 hydrogen, importation could be practical. Concrete made by mixing cement with lunar regolith and gravel will be very useful for construction within pressurized lava tubes someday. It cannot be used out-vac because the precious water will just evaporate into the vacuum and the chemical reactions that make the cement harden will not occur. Concrete items could be cast inside pressurized modules then moved outside. Cement board for walls inside of modules could be made indoors. It might even be possible to spray concrete inside of inflated forms to make habitat.

Concrete can be made from 1 part cement, 2 parts sand (raw regolith that has been sized by screening and sieving), and 4 parts gravel.[23] Thus, a meager amount of cement makes seven times as much concrete. Concrete floors inside pressurized inflatables will provide a sturdy base for heavy machines like large engine lathes weighing 24,000 pounds on Earth (4,000 lbs. on the Moon) and heavy parts like multi-ton steel rolls for rolling mills. It will also resist damage by spilled molten metals from small part casting.

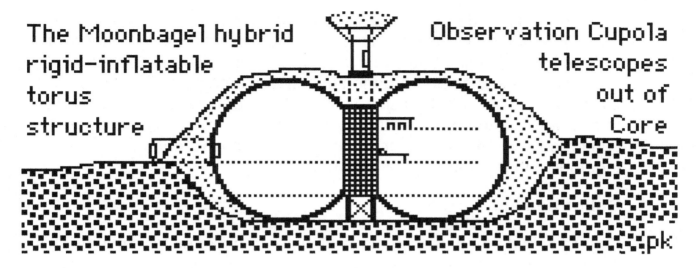

Fig. 6 Pressurized inflatable structure for making molds, machining metals and pouring concrete with sturdy concrete floor. Courtesy of Peter Kokh.

Martian Cement

Gypsum is found on Mars and there might be carbonates. Clays are also present on Mars. Gypsum could be broken down into lime, mixed with clay, and heated in solar or electrical furnaces to make clinker. This would be ground, mixed with gypsum and ground some more to make Portland cement. The air is too thin on Mars to pour cement outside, so cement casting would have to be done inside habitat and eventually inside pressurized Martian lava tubes.

Cement in Orbital or "Free" Space Settlements

Once a metal shell is constructed and pressurized, cement and concrete can be poured to make all sorts of structures inside. In Earth orbit, there should be plenty of calcium silicate materials left over after aluminum, magnesium and titanium are extracted from lunar regolith payloads for SSPS construction. Concrete is a fairly heavy material. Construction within space settlements might be done with lightweight autoclaved aerated concrete or AAC. This material only weighs about 20% as much as ordinary concrete and has about half as much compressive strength. It is made by mixing sand, cement, lime, water and a small amount of aluminum powder. The aluminum reacts with lime and water to form hydrogen gas bubbles that foam up the material. It is then cut into blocks or slabs and hardened in a steam autoclave. This material can be used for walls, furnishings, etc. It can be routed, sanded and cut to size with standard power tools. It is a good thermal insulator and it can be coated with plaster or stucco. Blocks of AAC can be bound together with standard cement mortar.

Sulfur Cement

Sulfur might also be used in place of water to make sulfur cement. This is made simply by mixing molten sulfur with sand. No lime is required. Sulfur cement can be mixed with gravel to make concrete.[24] Sulfur can be obtained by roasting large tonnages of lunar regolith at 900 to 1200 C. It has one drawback--it will melt in the heat of lunar day. Large foil heat shields will be required and we could cast sulfur cement structures in the shadow, perhaps with contour crafting gantries, to make structures that would then be covered with several meters of regolith for thermal insulation and radiation shielding for habitat stationed within the structures.

On Mars, it doesn't get hot enough to melt sulfur cement. Sulfur could come from sulfate minerals present on Mars.

The View Toward the Future

On Mars, mortar will be used inside of pressurized habitat to bond bricks made from Martian regolith. We can also mine gypsum, $CaSO_4*H_2O$, on Mars. On the Moon we will need to use mortar made from cement and sand which does not require CO_2 to harden to bond bricks made of sintered basalt perhaps in lava tubes. We will not want mortar to absorb CO_2 from the air of lava tube habitations because carbon is scarce on the Moon and we need it for supporting crops.

Leaching aluminous Highland regolith with sulfuric acid will be a job for more advanced Moon communities when we can manufacture the necessary equipment on the Moon and have water from polar ice mining and water made by combining hydrogen from solar wind implanted volatiles mining with LUNOX in abundance. We will need quite a bit of industry there to do the job. The original "seed packages" of robotic devices will grow and grow using lunar materials to make more equipment until we are ready to seal, pressurize and inhabit lava tubes. Inside the lava tubes, towns for several thousand people will be built with concrete, bricks, plaster, glass and metal mainly iron. There will be no intrusion by ground water on the Moon to erode or rust our structures. These underground towns will be more homey than the metal and inflatable plastic bases we build in the early days of lunar industrialization. They will have gardens and farm sections illuminated by light piped in from the surface during the long day and super efficient microwave sulfur lamps that mimic the spectrum of the Sun without the UV and IR by night.

The sulfuric acid leaching tanks and related equipment will be made with an alloy of abundant lunar iron and about 15% silicon called *duriron* instead of stainless steel. [25] Cast basalt also resists concentrated sulfuric acid and caustic bases like sodium hydroxide, so acid handling equipment might be made with cast basalt. Acid leaching will also produce plenty of silica for glass and calcium sulfate which is dry plaster. Plaster can be wetted and applied between two layers of glass fiber or basalt fiber cloth and allowed to harden to make a wallboard that resists moisture and mildew. We will not need precious paper for wallboard.

Prior to acid leaching, anorthosite must be melted and quenched to break down its crystalline structure. It must be melted to form an amorphous glass then cooled rapidly to prevent recrystallization. Since water cannot be wasted it might be possible to use liquid oxygen. Then the material can be broken up with hammers and ground fine in rod and ball mills. Liquid oxygen would never be used to quench hot metal because it would oxidize the metal, maybe even ignite it, but anorthosite is already oxidized so this might work.

Sulfur is present in regolith in the form of meteoric troilite, FeS, and perhaps other forms. The lunar dust roaster and all isotope separators can get the sulfur along with other elements present in mere parts per million. It's also possible to just roast the regolith at over 900 C. and sulfur will evaporate from the regolith. Sulfur will be used for sulfur cement, sulfuric acid and possibly sodium-sulfur batteries. It can be used for polymers too. It might be used to vulcanize synthetic rubber tires for vehicles that operate in pressurized lava tubes. Sulfuric acid can be used to remove scale from metals if that should be a problem.

Heat treating metals in salt pots might lead to scale formation. Sulfuric acid is used to make rayon, a semi-synthetic fiber. Carbon disulfide, also used to make rayon, is made by reacting sulfur and carbon in an electric arc furnace. Iron can be reacted with sulfuric acid to make a bluish green iron sulfate salt that might serve as a pigment for paint and ink. Aluminum sulfate is also called alum and it has numerous industrial uses. Magnesium sulfate is the familiar Epsom salts. Sulfur has other uses. Sulfur dioxide can be used as a refrigerant. However, it is toxic so importation of inert CFC or HFC refrigerants might be wiser. Ultramarine blue, a beautiful pigment, can be made by heating a mixture of sulfur, kaolinite clay and sodium carbonate in a kiln. Clays will not be found on the Moon, but they do exist on Mars. Since ultramarine consists of sulfur, sodium, silicon, aluminum and oxygen, all of which are found on the Moon in good quantities, clever chemists might figure out how to make ultramarine blue with only lunar resources.

Chemistry with Simple Feedstocks

Numerous substances like hydrogen, carbon monoxide and nitrogen can be obtained by solar wind implanted volatiles mining and polar ice mining on the Moon. On Mars, CO_2 and nitrogen can be extracted from the atmosphere and hydrogen can come from water ice. Many asteroids contain hydrocarbons. These can be reacted to make various chemicals and plastics. A mixture of hydrogen and carbon monoxide in the right proportions, pressures, temperatures and with the right catalysts can make almost any organic chemical. The mixture of hydrogen and CO is called synthesis gas or Syn-gas.

$2H_2 + CO \rightarrow CH_3OH$ $ZnO-Cr_2O_3$ catalyst used
                methanol

$CH_3OH + CO \rightarrow CH_3COOH$ 50 atm rhodium iodide catalyst 200° C.
                acetic acid

$CH_3OH + HCl \rightarrow CH_3Cl + H_2O$
              methyl chloride

$3H_2 + CO \rightarrow CH_4 + H_2O$ Ni catalyst used
             methane

$5H_2 + 2CO \rightarrow C_2H_6 + 2H_2O$
             ethane

So what does it all mean?

Hydrogen and CO gas can be reacted to form methanol. Methanol can be used as a solvent and it can be converted to formaldehyde which is used to make resins and plastics. In the commonly used Formox process, methanol and oxygen react at ca. 250–400 °C in the presence of iron oxide in combination with molybdenum and/or vanadium.[26] This produces formaldehyde according to the chemical equation:

$2\ CH_3OH + O_2 \rightarrow 2\ CH_2O + 2\ H_2O$

        formaldehyde

Methane is the most common component of natural gas. Unfortunately, it's not likely that natural gas exists on the Moon or Mars, but there is a lot of methane in gaseous and liquid form on Saturn's moon Titan. On the Moon or Mars, methane would be made from syngas made from various sources of light elements. Methane is mostly useful as a fuel that has a much higher boiling point than LH_2. It could be used as rocket fuel and it could be reacted with oxygen in fuel cells to make electricity for vehicle motors and waste heat that might be useful for warming pressurized cabins. The products are water and CO_2. These would have to be recaptured and recycled on the Moon because they aren't that plentiful even if we do mine polar ices. On Mars where CO_2 can be obtained by pumping down atmosphere this might not be as critical. Since CO and CO_2 are very stable and decompose at very high temperatures, it is easier to combine them with hydrogen to make methane which can then be decomposed at 900 C. to get pure carbon and hydrogen that can be recycled. Pure carbon can be used to make steel and it can be used for air and water filters. Incomplete combustion of carbon will yield CO gas for syngas.

Ethane is the second most common component of natural gas. Like methane, it won't be found underground on the Moon but there might be some in polar ices since it has been detected in comets. It's mostly used to make ethylene by steam cracking.[27] Ethane can be used as a refrigerant in cryogenic systems and it can be used in heat pipes that run too cold for ammonia.[28]

On the Moon ethylene could be made by directly combining hydrogen and CO in the right proportions or indirectly from methanol without making ethane first.

$$4H_2 + 2CO \rightarrow C_2H_4 + 2H_2O$$
$$\text{ethylene}$$

$$6H_2 + 3CO \rightarrow C_3H_6 + 3H_2O$$
$$\text{propylene}$$

Ethylene and propylene are called olefins (alkenes), which are compounds made of hydrogen and carbon that have one or more pairs of carbon atoms linked by a double bond. They are produced by cracking crude oil—something we can't do on the Moon or Mars because there is no oil. We must wonder about the possibility of heavier hydrocarbons resembling oil extant in the depths of the methane lakes of Titan. That would be a boon to space settlers. On Earth today, syngas from coal or natural gas is converted to methanol which is then converted to olefins, mostly ethylene and propylene. Zeolite catalysts are used. [29] Recent research has shown that syngas can be directly converted to olefins using zinc chromium oxide catalysts and zeolite catalysts.[30]

Ethylene and propylene are used to make polymers. Polyethylene and polypropylene are the two most common plastics in use today. Ethylene and propylene gases are compressed to high pressure in the presence of catalysts and polymerize. Plastics would not be discarded on the Moon or in space. They would be rigorously reused and recycled. Carbon, hydrogen, nitrogen and organic compounds from polar ice will be not be cheap enough for disposables; and why trash the Moon as we have trashed the oceans? The same applies to Mars and other worlds of the solar system.

Methanol can be reacted with HCl to make methyl chloride which can be reacted with silicon at 300° C. in the presence of a copper catalyst to make dimethyldichlorosilane $(CH_3)_2SiCl_2$. This can then be reacted with water to make silicone polymers and HCl which can be recycled because chlorine is rare on the Moon. Silicones can make lubricant oils, greases, caulk, waxes, and rubber.[31]

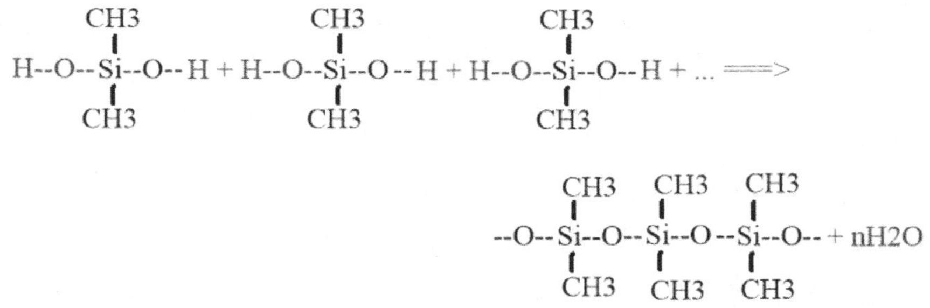

$$
\begin{array}{ccc}
CH_3 & CH_3 & CH_3 \\
| & | & | \\
H{-}O{-}Si{-}O{-}H + & H{-}O{-}Si{-}O{-}H + & H{-}O{-}Si{-}O{-}H + \ldots \Longrightarrow \\
| & | & | \\
CH_3 & CH_3 & CH_3
\end{array}
$$

$$
\begin{array}{ccc}
CH_3 & CH_3 & CH_3 \\
| & | & | \\
{-}O{-}Si{-}O{-} & Si{-}O{-} & Si{-}O{-} + nH2O \\
| & | & | \\
CH_3 & CH_3 & CH_3
\end{array}
$$

Silicone polymer

Fig. 7 $(CH_3)_2SiCl_2$ reacts with water to form $(CH_3)_2Si(OH)_2$ which then condenses to form silicone polymers.

Methanol can also be converted to acetic acid which is used to make acetic anhydride and acetate salts like calcium acetate.[32] Calcium acetate is made by reacting calcium metal, calcium hydroxide or calcium oxide with concentrated acetic acid.

Calcium acetate can be dry distilled to make acetone, another solvent that also makes nail polish remover, and calcium carbonate a.k.a. limestone. Limestone is not present on the Moon so it would have to be synthesized. It is useful as a flux in steel making and it can be used as a pH buffer in closed ecological life support systems. Acetone is also used for making numerous organic chemicals.

$$Ca(CH_3COO)_2 \rightarrow CaO(s) + CO_2(g) + (CH_3)_2CO$$

calcium acetate   acetone

$$(CH_3COO)_2Ca \xrightarrow{\Delta} CH_3COCH_3 + CaCO_3$$

Acetone   calcium carbonate

(limestone)

Acetone can dissolve plastics and some synthetic fibers. It is used as paint thinner and it is used in some paints and varnishes. It is a good solvent and can be used as heavy-duty degreaser. It is used as a solvent for vinyl and acrylic resins, lacquers, alkyd paints, and inks.[33] Acetone is used to make Plexiglas, polycarbonates, polyurethanes and expoxy resins.[34]

Most acetone today is made by the cumene process.[35] Benzene and propylene are reacted to form cumene which then reacts with oxygen in the air to form acetone and phenol. Phenol can be combined with formaldehyde to make Bakelite, a hard scratch resistant electrically and thermally insulating plastic that is seldom used today.[36] As described earlier, propylene can be made by combining carbon monoxide and hydrogen. Benzene is common in crude oil and coal tar on Earth but some might be found in lunar polar ices since benzene was detected in comet 67P/Churyumov-Gerasimenko by the Rosetta spacecraft along with toluene, butane, pentane, hexane and heptane.[37]

If benzene cannot be produced from ice it can be prepared from ethyne by the process of cyclic polymerization. In this process, ethyne is passed through a red hot iron tube at 873 K. The ethyne molecule then undergoes cyclic polymerization to form benzene.[38] Ethyne is more commonly called acetylene. Acetylene can be made by reacting calcium carbide with water (see below). Benzene is the starting compound for many products including polyester, aniline dyes, polyurethane, polycarbonate, epoxy resins, salicylic acid, nylon, polystyrene, rubber and more.

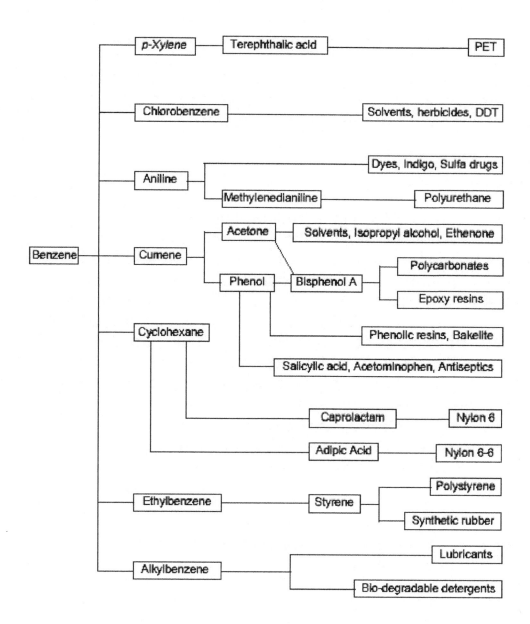

Fig. 8 Benzene has many uses.

$$H - C \equiv C - H$$

ethyne (acetylene)

$CaC_2 + 2H_2O \rightarrow Ca(OH)_2 + C_2H_2$
calcium carbide   acetylene

Calcium carbide reacts with water to make acetylene. Acetylene is used for Oxv-Acetylene welding and cutting. Acetylene gas is unstable and must be dissolved in acetone under pressure for safe storage.

Calcium carbide is produced industrially in an electric arc furnace from a mixture of lime and coke at approximately 2,200 °C (3,990 °F).[39] This method has not changed since its invention in 1892:

$CaO + 3\,C \rightarrow CaC_2 + CO$
             calcium carbide

Calcium is present on the Moon in the mineral anorthosite $CaAl_2Si_2O_8$ which composes most of the lunar highlands regolith. Anorthosite can be melted, quenched with LOX and ground fine in rod and ball mills then leached with sulfuric acid H_2SO_4 to form a solution of highly soluble aluminum sulfate and a precipitate of silicic acid and barely soluble calcium sulfate. These can be dried out and separated electrostatically. The silica gel can be used as is, melted to make glass or roasted with sodium oxide to make sodium silicate. The calcium sulfate is plaster for walls and molds. Plaster can be applied between sheets of woven glass fiber or perhaps basalt fiber to make drywall also known as sheetrock. The $CaSO_4$ can be roasted at about 1500° C. to form solid calcium oxide and gaseous oxides of sulfur. CaO could be electrolyzed in FFC cells to get calcium metal and oxygen.[40]

Acetylene reacts with anhydrous hydrogen chloride gas over a mercuric chloride catalyst to give vinyl chloride:

$C_2H_2 + HCl \rightarrow CH_2=CHCl$
                vinyl chloride

When heated to 500 °C at 15–30 atm (1.5 to 3 MPa) pressure, dichloroethane decomposes to produce vinyl chloride and anhydrous HCl.

$$ClCH_2CH_2Cl \xrightarrow{\hspace{1cm}} CH_2{=}CHCl + HCl$$
dichloroethane   vinyl chloride

Due to the relatively low cost of dichloroethane compared to acetylene, most vinyl chloride has been produced via this technique since the late 1950s.[41] Nearly 20 million tons of 1,2-dichloroethane are produced in the United States, Western Europe, and Japan annually.[42] Production is primarily achieved through the iron(III) chloride-catalysed reaction of ethylene and chlorine:

$$H_2C{=}CH_2 \text{ (g)} + Cl_2 \text{ (g)} \rightarrow ClCH_2{-}CH_2Cl \text{ (l)}$$
ethylene   dichloroethane

Vinyl chloride is polymerized to make PVC or "Vinyl" plastic which was once used to make LP records and furniture including car seats. Polyvinyl chloride abbreviated PVC is the world's third-most widely produced synthetic plastic polymer,
after polyethylene and polypropylene. About 40 million tonnes are produced per year.[43]

Nitrogen and Ammonia

Nitrogen is present in Earth's atmosphere. It can be obtained by fractional distillation of liquid air. There is some nitrogen from the solar wind implanted in lunar regolith and it is also present in lunar polar ices in the form of ammonia (NH_3). The atmosphere of Mars contains a small amount of nitrogen that could be obtained by fractional distillation of liquefied Martian atmospheric gases. The atmospheres of the outer planets and the ices of some of their moons contain ammonia.

Nitrogen is necessary for atmospheres and fertilizer. Humans have survived in pure oxygen atmospheres, but the long-term effects of this are unknown. It seems safe to say that atmospheres in space settlements should contain some nitrogen. Many legumes, most famously the peanut, have nitrogen fixing bacteria in their root nodules that can take nitrogen from the air and put it in the ground. Crop rotation with legumes makes it possible to prevent nitrogen exhaustion of the soil. Without nitrogen, plants cannot make protein.

Dry ammonia is used directly as fertilizer or in the form of compounds like ammonium sulfate or ammonium nitrate. Ammonium sulfate can be made by reacting ammonia with sulfuric acid and ammonium nitrate by reaction of ammonia with nitric acid. Since ammonia from comets exists in lunar polar ice we can use that for fertilizer. It could be obtained by melting and distilling the ice. Nitrogen from the lunar regolith or the Martian atmosphere can be reacted with hydrogen to make ammonia.

Nitrogen and hydrogen can be combined by using the Haber-Bosch process at a pressure of 200 bar and a temperature of 500 C. in the presence of an iron or ruthenium based catalyst.[44] This requires a complex arrangement of pipes, pumps, compressors, reaction vessels and heat exchangers. Making all this in space from on-site resources will be quite a challenge.

Space Chemistry's Future

Some might ask, why produce plastics when you have plenty of metal, glass and basalt? We need synthetic fibers, rubber washers, plastic O-ring seals, flexible hoses, sealants, caulks, gaskets, toys, space helmets (polycarbonate), space suits, electrical wire insulation, varnish for electric motor coils, rubber gloves and PPE, disposable medical supplies, food wrapping and lots of other things. These would all be reused or recycled.

The Moon is not nearly as rich in light elements like hydrogen, carbon, chlorine and nitrogen as the Earth is. Many terrestrial chemicals are derived directly from oil. Others are produced from coal, natural gas or biowaste. Nitrogen can be liquefied out of the air and chlorine can be obtained from salt deposits and seawater in abundance.

Mars might not have oil, gas and coal but it does have plenty of water in permafrost, a thin atmosphere of carbon dioxide and nitrogen, and chlorine bearing perchlorates in the regolith of the red planet. Martians could make use of some of the same chemical strategies that will be used on the Moon.

While the Moon might not ever produce enough chemicals and plastics for populations of billions, or even mere millions, there should be enough HCN from solar wind implanted volatiles and polar ices to make enough chemicals and plastics for industry in space. In the more distant future, light elements on the Moon and in space will be derived from asteroid hydrocarbons. Carbonaceous chondrite asteroids contain a tarry substance that resembles kerogen along with significant amounts of water. Rather than mine all the regolith of the Moon and extract all the polar ice it would seem wise to conserve those resources for future generations and make use of water and hydrocarbons from asteroids when space industry has grown large enough to economically mine those asteroids and transport the materials through space in interplanetary cargo and tanker ships.

Benzene and Derivatives

Benzene is one of the top 20 industrial chemicals in terms of production volume. In 2019, about 4.7 million metric tons were produced in the U.S.[45] It is a precursor to many other plastics and chemicals and will find use in space. Unfortunately, natural sources of benzene like oil and coal don't exist on the Moon or Mars. Whether or not it can be derived from asteroid hydrocarbons which often contain aromatic compounds is unknown. As stated earlier, benzene can be produced by passing acetylene through a red hot iron pipe at 600 C. (873 K.). Acetylene can be produced by reacting water with calcium carbide. Calcium carbide can be produced by heating lime and carbon in an electric arc or solar furnace at 2,200 C. Water and carbon are scarce on the Moon and will probably exist in limited supplies in space habitat. Mars has relatively large resources of water and carbon by comparison. Even so, making plastics and such will be limited by the scarcity of resources. The largest use of plastics in space might be the manufacturing of space suits. These probably won't be made at early mining bases, but as the population in space grows it would seem that making space suits on-site would become more economical than importing them from Earth.

Dacron is used in spacesuits. Dacron is a thermoplastic polymer material of the polyester family. Polyester is the name given to a group of materials, whereas Dacron is a brand name of polyethylene terephthalate (PET). PET is also used to make disposable drink bottles, but this won't be done in space. Drink bottles will be made of glass or basalt and they will be returned for a deposit, washed and sterilized, and reused. Some clothing is made of polyester but there probably won't be a lot of that. Dacron will require terephthalic acid or dimethyl terephthalate (DMT). Terephthalic acid is made by the catalytic oxidation of para-xylene.[46] A mixture of *p*-xylene, acetic acid, a cobalt-manganese-bromide catalyst and compressed air or a mixture of CO_2 and oxygen are fed into a reactor made of titanium that can stand up to corrosion by these substances. Oxygen, CO_2, and acetic acid can be produced on the Moon and so can titanium. Bromides would have to be imported. But where to get *p*-xylene?

Benzene seems to be the most likely starting point for *p*-xylene, unless some other chemical of cometary origin is present in lunar polar ice. Mars doesn't have cometary ice deposits, so benzene could be used there. Ethylbenzene can be converted to *p*-xylene by a patented process that uses platinum and zeolite catalysts.[47] Ethylbenzene can be made by reacting benzene and ethylene in the presence of an acid catalyst. It is also possible to convert benzene to toluene then convert toluene to xylene. Converting benzene to toluene requires methyl chloride and aluminum chloride, so lunar or imported chlorine is needed. Mars has plenty of chlorine. Methyl chloride can be made by reacting methanol with HCl and methanol can be gotten from hydrogen and carbon monoxide. Toluene has also been detected in comets so there might be some in lunar polar ices. Toluene can be combined with methanol to make *p*-xylene. [48]

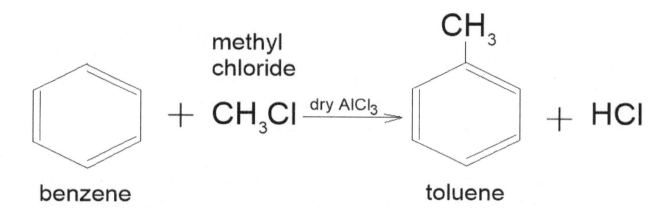

Fig. 9 Benzene can be reacted with methyl chloride to make toluene and hydrogen chloride. The HCl can be reacted with methanol to make more methyl chloride and recycle the scarce chlorine.

That all sounds fairly simple, but in reality complex arrangements of pipes, pumps, compressors, valves, distillation or fractionating towers, drying columns, and more are needed to make everything happen. Chemical engineers will have to design this equipment and manufacturing engineers will have to figure out how to make it with local resources. Terephthalic acid can also be derived by oxidizing Caraway oil, but can space farms produce enough Caraway seeds? If the DMT process is chosen, then terephthalic acid has to be reacted with methanol to make DMT, and that won't be as simple as saying that. Terephthalic acid or DMT must be reacted with ethylene glycol to make PET. Ethylene glycol is made by reacting ethylene oxide with water and ethylene oxide is made by oxidizing ethylene in the presence of a silver catalyst.

All that to make polyester, Dacron, and many details of the various processes involved have been left out of this discussion. Polyester can also be used in the production of Spandex, so PET comes before Spandex. Mylar is just a stretched film of PET. The purpose of this discussion is to indicate that the necessary chemicals, with the exception of some of the catalysts which would have to be imported from Earth, can be obtained on the Moon and Mars and perhaps other worlds in space.

Benzene could also be reacted with chlorine in the presence of catalytic ferric chloride, sulfur dichloride or aluminum chloride to make chlorobenzene. Chlorobenzene is a solvent and it is an intermediate in the production of herbicides, dyes and rubber. It was used in the past to make phenol and also DDT. There won't be much use for DDT in space farms unless some ravenous bugs make their way into space. If DDT was used, there are not likely to be many birds in the space farm that would be harmed.

Aniline can be made by reacting benzene with nitric and sulfuric acids to get nitrobenzene. This is then reacted with hydrogen in the presence of metallic catalysts to make aniline.[49] Aniline is used to make methylenedianiline, a precursor to polyurethane, by reaction with formaldehyde. Polyurethane is one of the many materials used to make spacesuits. It's a good thermal insulator. Indigo dyes like the ones used to make blue jeans blue, some antibiotic sulfa drugs, rubber antioxidants and the pain killer acetaminophen are made from aniline or its derivatives.

Benzene and propylene can be reacted in a maze of pipes and reactor vessels at 30 atm and 250 C. in the presence of phosphoric acid to make cumene, which can then be oxidized to cumene hydroperoxide and hydrolyzed in an acid bath to make phenol and acetone. Phenol and acetone have many uses. Two mols of phenol can be reacted with one mol of acetone to make one mol of bisphenol-A (BPA). This compound is used to make polycarbonate, a hard, impact resistant, transparent plastic used to make space helmets. BPA is also used to make epoxy resins. Phenol is also reacted with formaldehyde to make Bakelite, a hard, scratch resistant, insulating plastic. Phenolic resins continue to be used for a wide variety of applications, such as moulding powders, laminating resins, adhesives, binders, surface coatings and impregnants. Phenol is also used as an antiseptic and for the making of acetaminophen and salicylic acid.

Aspirin, acetylsalicylic acid, is made by reacting salicylic acid with acetic anhydride. Making acetic anhydride is discussed in the next chapter. Methyl salicylate, an ester of salicylic acid, for topical use to ease the pain of bruises and sore joints is made by reacting salicylic acid with methanol. It's also found in oil of Wintergreen. Salicylic acid can be used topically to fight acne, dandruff and warts. But where do we get salicylic acid?

Salicylic acid is made by reacting phenol with sodium hydroxide to form sodium phenoxide which is then reacted with CO_2 at high pressure (100 atm) and high temperature (115 C.) and acidified with sulfuric acid to yield salicylic acid. Sodium hydroxide can be made on the Moon by simply reacting sodium metal with water, a reaction which releases lots of heat and hydrogen so it shouldn't be done in air, or by electrolysis of sodium chloride solutions in a Castner-Kellner cell. This will require imported mercury. Sodium hydroxide has other uses including soap production.

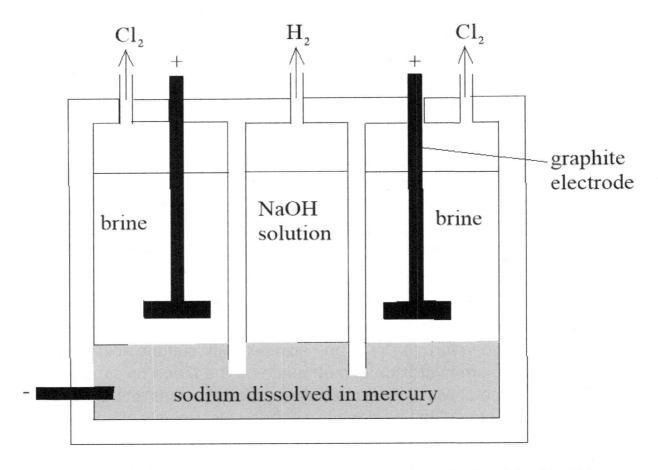

Fig. 10 Castner-Kellner cell for making sodium hydroxide, NaOH.

Carbon dioxide, sulfuric acid, sodium hydroxide and methanol in addition to benzene will also be common substances used by space industry. Acetone will also be derived from benzene via the cumene process. This substance is a good solvent and degreaser, paint thinner, nail polish remover and it can dissolve cellulose acetate for pouring into molds or making filaments. It can dissolve Superglue. Acetone is also used to make acrylics like Plexiglas. Excess acetone can be turned into isopropyl alcohol by hydrogenation. This is the kind of rubbing alcohol we find in drug stores these days....ethyl alcohol gets you drunk and methyl alcohol (methanol) can make you go blind. Acetone can also be used to make ketene (ethenone) for making acetic anhydride which is used to make aspirin and cellulose acetate. Acetone is used extensively as a solvent for the safe transportation and storage of acetylene, which cannot be safely pressurized as a pure compound. Vessels containing a porous material are first filled with acetone followed by acetylene, which dissolves into the acetone. One liter of acetone can dissolve around 250 liters of acetylene at a pressure of 10 bar. Oxy-acetylene torches are good for cutting through metal, although most welding in space would be electric arc, laser, friction stir and ultrasonic. We would also want a way to store acetylene for conversion to benzene, so it's good to have acetone.

Benzene is the main raw material for the industrial production of Nylon 6 and Nylon 66. Nylon is also used in spacesuits and has many more everyday clothing uses. Benzene is converted to cyclohexane by reacting it with hydrogen in the presence of a Raney-nickel catalyst.[50] Cyclohexane is a precursor to both caprolactam used to make Nylon 6 and adipic acid used to make Nylon 66.[51]

Benzene is converted to ethylbenzene by reacting benzene with ethylene in the presence of zeolite catalysts. Ethylbenzene is dehydrogenated to make styrene. Styrene is used to make polystyrene plastic, ABS, styrene-butadiene rubber (SBR), styrene-butadiene latex, SIS (styrene-isoprene-styrene), S-EB-S (styrene-ethylene/butylene-styrene), styrene-divinylbenzene (S-DVB), styrene-acrylonitrile resin (SAN), and unsaturated polyesters. These materials are used to make rubber, plastic, insulation, pipes, car and boat parts, fiberglass, food containers, and carpet backing.[52]

Alkylbenzenes include toluene, ortho, meta and para-xylenes, ethylbenzene, cumene and para-cymene. The production of some of these was discussed earlier. Alkylbenzene oils are used as lubricants in refrigeration compressors and linear alkylbenzene sulfonates are used as biodegradable detergents.[53] We must wonder how these detergents would effect CELSS in which black water is degraded biologically.

The value of benzene in space is clear. If many of the products of daily life on Earth from aspirin to nylon clothing, and products needed in space like spacesuits, are to be had on the Moon, Mars or in free space habitat, then benzene is a necessity. Unless asteroid hydrocarbons can be a source of benzene, or large amounts are found in lunar polar ices, benzene will have to be made from acetylene produced by reacting calcium carbide with water. Storing acetylene will require acetone, but this seems like a hitch when we need benzene and propylene to make acetone via the cumene process. Fortunately, acetone can be made by the distillation of acetate salts made by reacting metals with acetic acid. Acetic acid can be made by reacting methanol with CO gas along with a rhodium iodide catalyst. Thus, it will be possible to make acetone for storing acetylene intended for conversion to benzene before we start using the cumene process.

Natural and Semi-synthetic Materials

As stated earlier, the Moon and Mars have no oil, coal or natural gas. They don't have any trees either. Traces of water, carbon oxides, hydrogen, nitrogen and some helium exist in the lunar regolith. Polar ices in permanently shadowed lunar craters may contain these and other chemicals found in comets. Mars has plenty of water in permafrost and CO_2 and nitrogen in its atmosphere. Martians will find it easier to produce organic chemicals for plastics, medicines, paint, lubricants and such than lunar inhabitants will. Lunans will have to use metals like aluminum, magnesium and titanium along with some pure iron, glass, basalt and ceramics for most things. Steel will be limited by the carbon supply. Fortunately, a small amount of carbon makes a large amount of steel. Due to the non-existence of oil, coal and gas on the Moon and the small supply of H, C and N, plastics and silicones will be used only when necessary on the Moon and they will be carefully recycled. We will make use of compostable bio-plastics also. The H, C and N for plastics and silicones will come from regolith and polar ice, but those are slim pickens'. Some C-type asteroids contain a tarry hydrocarbon material and these asteroids might become the major source of light elements for organic chemicals for the Moon and free space habitat someday. Saturn's moon Titan and the ices of the moons of the outer planets and even the atmospheres of the giant planets might serve as sources of H, C and N someday too.

Such is life in worlds without oil, coal and gas. No trees means we are not going to have lots of paper and no wood. There could someday be trees in lunar and Martian settlements within pressurized lava tubes and huge domes. There could be trees in free space habitat. It is unlikely that these trees will be numerous enough to provide wood and paper, but they might supply some fruit. Other than that, trees in space settlements will exist mostly for decorative purposes and for recycling CO_2 to oxygen.

While documents and business transactions can all be electronic, we must have toilet paper. Bamboo and hemp may be our sources of paper for bathroom tissue. Basically, you just grind up the fibrous material, mix it with water and maybe some soda ash, cook it to get pulp, roll out the pulp in sheets and bake it. Sometimes additives are used. Bamboo, hemp and possibly even algae could supply cellulose for paper. Writing and drawing can be done with computers and signs can be made by applying paint to metal, glass or ceramic sheet, but some writing and drawing paper will be nice to have. As for bathroom tissue made from bamboo, it's already available on Amazon and the stuff is as soft as tree paper. All discarded paper products will be rigorously recycled. To buy a newspaper, one may have to turn in an old newspaper. As for the bath tissue, it will go down into the black water system, be degraded biologically or mechanically, and turned into plant nutrient solution for more bamboo and hemp crops. Some species of bamboo can grow 36 inches in 24 hours, so a small bamboo forest can be very productive. So much for life without trees.

Chemical factories will emerge from Nature's nanobots brought to the Moon, Mars and beyond--seeds and spores. Plants and algae are natural chemical factories that can take simple feedstocks like CO_2, water, minerals and sunlight and make all kinds of substances like oils, lubricants, resins, tannins, natural rubber, gums, waxes, dyes, inks, flavors and fragrances, pharmaceuticals, and pesticides. They can supply natural fibers for clothing and linen. Of course, we must have the right shelter, atmosphere, lighting, temp. control, etc. Plants, algae and maybe some mushrooms and yeasts will make our chemicals and semi-synthetic materials for us instead of oil refineries and intimidating stainless steel chemical factories. When Nature doesn't provide, we might use some genetically modified organisms. Space farming is central to survival and prosperity in space for humans.

We must have plants for food and water, waste and air recycling. We also need them for clothes. Cotton, hemp, flax, etc. The problem is that these will sink carbon and water from the recycling loop, so we will need to obtain water and carbon by mining. Eventually, we will have worn out clothes that have been ripped and recycled so many times they can only be composted and their elements returned to the closed loop. It might also be possible to decompose the cloth and other materials with a super high temperature electric plasma arc that turns them back into their constituent elements.

There is a company called Bolt Threads that can make a leather substitute from fungus and spider silk from GMO yeast. So we don't need cows for leather. Will we want spider silk? Would we want silkworms? Would we want artificial silk also known as rayon for clothing and bedsheets? Would we want cellulose acetate like the stuff they use for Warby Parker eyeglasses?

We could make them. For rayon, cellulose is extracted from cotton, wood or straw. On the Moon and Mars, bamboo might be the best stuff to get cellulose from. The bamboo would be macerated to make a pulp that is then dissolved in a solution of sodium hydroxide to form a brown pulp solution of alkali cellulose. This is washed and bleached, then mixed with carbon disulfide to form cellulose xanthate. The mixture is then dissolved in a sodium hydroxide solution to make "viscose." The viscose is then pushed through a device with tiny holes in it called a spinneret to make filaments of regenerated cellulose. The filaments are solidified in a bath of sulfuric acid and spun into yarn that can be knitted or woven into fabric.[54] If it is precipitated in sheets instead of fibers it makes the product known as cellophane.

Sodium hydroxide (NaOH, caustic soda) can be made from lunar sodium and water. Carbon disulfide (CS_2) is made just by roasting carbon and sulfur in an electric arc furnace. Sulfuric acid and be made from sulfur, oxygen and water with a vanadium pentoxide catalyst.

Cellulose acetate is a bit more involved. The cellulose is reacted with a mixture of acetic acid and acetic anhydride to form cellulose acetate which is then dissolved in acetone and drawn into fibers or cast into shapes. To get acetic acid we react hydrogen and carbon monoxide to make methanol then react methanol with CO to make acetic acid. Special catalysts are needed. We can react acetic acid with lime to get calcium acetate which can be dry distilled to make acetone. Acetone can also be made from benzene by a somewhat more complex process. Where do we get acetic anhydride, a chemical also used to make aspirin and other things? This is where things get more involved.

From Wikipedia we find: "acetic anhydride is also prepared by the reaction of ketene (ethenone) with acetic acid at 45–55 °C and low pressure (0.05–0.2 bar)."

$$H_2C=C=O + CH_3COOH \rightarrow (CH_3CO)_2O$$

ethenone   acetic acid   acetic anhydride

Well, we know how to make acetic acid, but where do we get ketene (ethenone)? One way is by pyrolysis of acetone. Vapors of acetone can be passed through hot pipes or hot wires at 500-600 C. with a little CS_2 mixed in. The acetone decomposes into methane and ethenone with a 95% yield.

$$\overset{\displaystyle H}{\underset{\displaystyle H_2C}{|}}\!-\!\overset{\displaystyle CH_3}{\underset{\displaystyle C}{|}}\!=\!O \xrightarrow{heat} H_2C=C=O + CH_4$$

acetone   ethenone

Another way to make ethenone is by the dehydration of acetic acid at 700-750 degrees Celsius (the Schmidlin-Bergman-Wilsmore reaction).[55]

$$\overset{\displaystyle H}{\underset{\displaystyle H_2C}{|}}\!-\!\overset{\displaystyle OH}{\underset{\displaystyle C}{|}}\!=\!O \xrightarrow{AlPO4} H_2C=C=O + H_2O$$

acetic acid   ethenone

Well, we know how to get acetone and carbon disulfide. We know how to make acetic acid too. Thus, we can get ketene (ethenone) by acetone pyrolysis. Seems we need an aluminum phosphate catalyst for the Schmidlin-Bergman-Wilsmore reaction to make ketene (ethenone) if we choose this method. The Moon has phosphorus along with lots of aluminum and oxygen. The mineral apatite, $3Ca_3(PO_4)_2 \bullet Ca(F,Cl)_2$, separated from regolith by electrophoresis perhaps, can be reacted with sulfuric acid to get a $CaSO_4$ precipitate and a mixture of phosphoric, hydrochloric and hydrofluoric acids that can be separated by distillation.

$$3Ca_3(PO_4)_2 \bullet Ca(F,Cl)_2 + H_2SO_4 \dashrightarrow H_3PO_4 + HF + HCl + CaSO_4$$

Aluminum phosphate ($AlPO_4$) can be made by reacting aluminum with phosphoric acid. This acid would also be used to make fertilizer.

In the previous chapters, "Chemistry with Simple Feedstocks" and "Benzene and Derivatives," I discussed making methanol, acetic acid, acetone, ethylene, PVC and other organic chemicals. This will require a small chemical factory or laboratory where small but significant amounts of these chemicals can be made according to our needs on the Moon, Mars and in space. It could be made mostly from on-site resources. The lab could be made of pipes, valves, reaction chambers and even pump housings and impellors made of basalt. Basalt does not burn even in pure oxygen and it resists 98% sulfuric acid solutions, 30% caustic solutions and doesn't react with organic chemicals like benzene, acetone or methanol. It is easy to mine from mare regolith on the Moon and it is also found on Mars. It can be melted and cast or drawn into fibers. It can also be sintered. Harvesting meteoric iron-nickel fines that can be alloyed with chromium from the Moon will allow the production of stainless steel. Steel could be cast, machined or shaped by selective laser sintering, a form of 3D printing, to make all sorts of parts. Glass can also be used for parts of the chemical lab. Titanium might also be used for corrosion resistant equipment and high pressure oxygen tanks. Electrical equipment could be made from aluminum wires and cables. Nichrome and Kanthal (Fe-Cr-Al) could be made for electric heating. Carbon electrodes for the electric arc furnaces may have to be imported. Since solar furnaces can reach extremely high temperatures like 4000 K. to 6000 K. it might be possible to use solar furnaces instead of electric arc furnaces to make calcium carbide and carbon disulfide, thereby negating the cost of importing carbon electrodes.

Chemistry and chemical engineering are vast subjects. We have only scratched the surface. Future inhabitants of the Moon, Mars and other worlds of the solar system will find and use the materials needed for survival and prosperity on the high frontier. Have no doubt.

Biomaterials

Space farms can supply more than just food. Useful substances can be made from crops. One of the first things we can think of are vegetable oils. Many vegetable oils are used to make paints, lubricants, hydraulic fluid, soaps, skin products, candles, perfumes and other personal care and cosmetic products. Oils can be pressed out of algae, soybeans, corn, sunflower seeds, cotton seeds, hemp seeds, flax seeds (linseed oil), jojoba seeds and castor beans. Using these oils for industry will take carbon out of the CELSS loop so we will have to add some CO_2 from the atmosphere on Mars and polar ice or solar wind implanted volatiles mining on the Moon to the habitat atmosphere to maintain CO_2 levels for plants and algae.

Soap can be made by reacting oils with strong bases like sodium hydroxide (lye) or potassium hydroxide. Animal fats can also be used to make soap. The base reacts with oils and fats to form glycerin and salts of stearic, palmitic and oleic fatty acids.[56]

$$(C_{17}H_{35}COO)_3C_3H_5 + 3\ NaOH ==> 3\ C_{17}H_{35}COONa + C_3H_5(OH)_3$$
Glyceryl Stearate   Sodium stearate   Glycerin

Soap is separated from glycerin and water by adding NaCl. This causes the soap to "salt out." It floats on top of the glycerin and water and forms a crust that is removed, dried and pressed into cakes. Glycerin can be used for lotions, cough
syrups, elixirs and expectorants, toothpaste, mouthwashes, skin care products, shaving cream, hair care products, soaps, and water-based personal lubricants. Glycerin is also used in blood banking to preserve red blood cells prior to freezing.[57]

Vegetable oils are biodegradable and have high flash points. They also oxidize easily. Castor oil is more resistant to oxidation than other vegetable oils. Castor oil and its derivatives are used in the manufacturing of soaps, lubricants, hydraulic and brake fluids, paints, dyes, coatings, inks, cold resistant plastics, waxes and polishes, nylon, pharmaceuticals and perfumes.[58] Hydraulic and brake fluids will not be exposed to oxygen or high temperatures so the lack of oxidative stability for vegetable oils is less problematic in these applications. Jojoba oil or wax has better oxidation resistance than most vegetable oils but not as much as castor oil. In 1943, natural resources of the U.S, including jojoba oil, were used during war as additives to motor oil, transmission oil and differential gear oil. Machine guns were lubricated and maintained with jojoba.[59]

Bioplastics can also be made. Polylactic Acid (PLA) is the most common bioplastic today. It is made by fermenting corn starch or sugar to make lactic acid which is then polymerized sometimes with the help of a zeolite catalyst.[60] The main shortcoming of PLA is its low glass transition temperature. This is the temperature at which it will transform from a rigid or glass-like substance to a soft and viscous material. For PLA this happens at 111 F. to 145 F. Boiling hot drinks or a hot car in the summer could cause it to soften and deform. PLA melts at 157 C. to 170 C. or 315 F. to 338 F. PLA is biodegradable and compostable.[61] Used dirty PLA items can just be macerated and tossed in the garbage, compost heap or bioreactors.

Corn starch can be extracted by milling, grinding, washing and drying corn kernels. Starch can be mixed with water, glycerin and acetic acid then heated to form a bioplastic similar to PLA that can be poured into molds. Agar extracted from algae can be mixed with water and glycerin in a similar manner to produce bioplastic. Alternatively potato starch can be used. Potato starch is easier to make than corn starch. Simply grate some potatoes. Soak them in water. Strain off the water and let the solution dry leaving starch. [62]

Paper can be made from almost any kind of cellulose plant fiber. Rice, hemp, straw, peanut shells, bamboo and perhaps other plants can serve as fiber sources. Paper can be recycled basically the same way it is made.[63] Paper can be shredded, mixed with water and mixed in a high speed blender to make pulp which is then drained from a screen and allowed to dry in air or with the help of a low temperature oven. With paper available, artists may desire paint. Paint can be made with mixtures of flour, salt, water, sometimes egg yolks, vegetable dyes and minerals like sulfur for yellow, iron oxide for rust, cobalt for blue. Milk protein can also be reacted with lime (CaO) to make paint. Many DIY paint making websites exist.

Cotton, flax and hemp can be cultivated to make clothing worn next to the skin. When clothes wear out they can be ripped and recycled and even composted. Basalt fiber cloth is actually rather smooth unlike glass fiber and can be used to make outerwear. There are other sources of materials for clothing, shoes and accessories. A completely vegan substitute for leather can be made from fungus mycelium grown on agricultural wastes and byproducts called Mylo.™ [64]

Bolt Threads, the company that makes Mylo™ also makes fibers from spider silk protein obtained from genetically programmed yeast called Microsilk.™ [65] Vats of fungal mycelium and yeast will free up space farm area that would otherwise be used for cotton, hemp, flax, etc. This will also be far more practical than herding cattle for hides in space or on the Moon and Mars.

Bamboo is a useful fast growing crop. Some species can grow 36 inches in 24 hours. Bamboo can be used to reinforce concrete. It has been used traditionally for medicine in Asia and it can be used instead of wood to build houses and schools. Bamboo shoots can feed people and animals. It can be used to make furniture, rugs, toys, kitchen utensils, beer and musical instruments like flutes and drums. Bamboo can make flooring, writing surfaces, pulp for paper making, fishing poles, and filters that can remove salt from seawater. [66] Such filters might be used in reverse osmosis pumps that work to control water salinity in Closed Ecological Life Support Systems or CELSS.

It has been claimed that bamboo can make cloth for bedding, clothing, accessories and diapers. However, according to Wikipedia, the FTC and the Canadian Competition Bureau bamboo textiles are actually rayon made from bamboo treated with harsh chemicals. Bamboo textiles are not made of natural fibers, but bamboo is a good source of cellulose for rayon if that is desired.[67]

Many drugs and medicines can be made from plants. Atropine, codeine, cocaine, caffeine, digitalis, ephedrine, quinine, morphine, reserpine and many other drugs/medicines come from plants.[68] Extracts can be made with water, ethanol or glycerin.

One of the most sought after biomaterials will be ethanol in the form of beer, wine and liqour. Pure concentrated ethanol can be used as an antiseptic and a solvent. It's just a matter of fermentation and distillation.

Toxic chemicals in a closed environment must be avoided. Aerosol spray cans are out. Roll ons and pump sprays for things like deodorants and perfumes could be used exclusively. Perfumes can be made from essential oils from roses, lavender, jasmine, carnations, chamomile, etc. These oils can be extracted with water, ethanol or vegetable oil. Many DIY natural perfume making websites exist.

Vegetable dyes can also be used for clothing. Red cabbages will make purple, onions will make yellow/orange, coffee grounds will make brown, and strawberries will make pink. Salt or vinegar (dilute acetic acid) can be used as fixatives (mordants).[69,70]

Rocket Propellant

Propellant from Space

The first step on the long road to lunar tourism, Mars settlement and space settlement is the creation of a manned reusable space plane that can put a person in low Earth orbit for a few tens of thousands of dollars. It would probably be powered by liquid hydrogen and use a combination of jet engines and rocket motors. Such a vehicle could fly people half-way around the world in less than an hour as well as carry people up to space hotels in low and medium Earth orbit. Space hotels would probably be made of inflatable modules at first. Small vessels based on inflatables with heat shields could be fueled up in orbit with hydrogen and oxygen from Earth's surface. These vessels could fly around the Moon and aerobrake into Earth orbit upon return. This is how lunar tourism would begin. Overflights will not be enough for some adventurers. Landings might take place in open cockpit vehicles.

Growth of the industry will eventually require more propellant obtained on the Moon and from near Earth asteroids. High thrust (compared to electric drives) rockets will be needed to travel from low Earth orbit to a space station at Earth-Moon Lagrange point one in just a few days' time. Solar electric spacecraft would spend weeks even months spiraling out to the Moon. Although such craft would use very little reaction mass, life support constraints and radiation exposure in the Van Allen Belts would make it impossible to use low thrust electric propulsion with manned vessels. Cargoes would be sent to the Moon and bases would be "bootstrapped" using local resources. It is not likely that the Moon will be colonized and industrialized for tourism alone. It is more likely that lunar resources will be tapped for the construction of solar power satellites and/or helium 3 mining. Tourism would ride in on the coat tails of the space energy industry. Mass drivers on the Moon capable of launching millions of tons of raw material into space every year could supply propellant to depots at Earth Moon Lagrange pt. 1 and in LEO. Hydrogen and oxygen would come from lunar polar ices at first and later from asteroids.

The infrastructure needed to support a commercial space travel industry will be very impressive. A multitude of lunar industrial settlements where humans and robots work together to extract metals and oxygen from Moon rocks and regolith will be needed along with bases on polar crater rims that send robots down into the darkness of the crater bottoms to mine for ice. Dozens of near Earth asteroids will be mined for water, carbon compounds, metals and oxygen someday. Large automated tankers will move mammoth quantities of rocket fuel and oxidizer through space.

Orbital propellant depots where rocket propellant is produced, stored and piped into spaceships will be needed in LEO, GEO, at EML1 and/or LLO. There may be dozens of them to handle all the traffic. Huge solar panel arrays will be needed to power all the cryogenic equipment, electrolyzers, furnaces, pumps and such. The depots would be built from lunar materials and expended external tanks.

To get an idea of how much propellant will be needed, let's envision a thousand spaceships each with a mass of one hundred tons empty and able to carry one hundred passengers. They would take three days to reach the Moon, or more accurately the transportation hub station at EML1, spend twelve hours refueling and being checked out, then travel back to LEO in three days where another twelve hours is devoted to servicing them. This means one round trip per week per ship. If these ships spend two weeks of every year in "dry dock" so that they can be refurbished with new engines and other equipment, they can each make fifty flights per year. One thousand of them could move five million tourists every year. That's about as many people that travel by air every day globally at the present time.

If these ships use nuclear thermal rocket engines, a risk that might be acceptable if the ships never enter the Earth's atmosphere, with a specific impulse of 1000 seconds and the delta V from LEO to L1 is 4100 meters per second then 52 tons of LH_2 will be required for one leg of the flight. If chemical propulsion using LH_2 and LOX is used, 153 tons of propellant will be needed. If silane and LOX with a specific impulse of 340 seconds is used then 242 tons of propellant are required. *The interesting thing about this is that chemical propulsion will use more propellant overall but less hydrogen than nuclear propulsion will.* With LH_2 and LOX, an Isp of 450 seconds, and a six to one oxidizer to fuel ratio, 22 tons of hydrogen will be necessary. With silane only ten tons of hydrogen, less than half as much, is needed as with hydrogen and LOX and only a fifth as much as is needed with nuclear.

Propellant Demands for 100 tons ship and a delta V of 4100 m/s

Nuclear rocket Isp 1000 sec. Exhaust velocity = 0.0098(1000) = 9.8 km/sec $e^{(4.1/9.8)}$ = 1.52

152/100 = 1.52   152-100= 52 tons LH_2

LH_2/LOX rocket Isp 450 sec. Exhaust velocity = 4.41 km/sec. $e^{(4.1/4.41)}$ = 2.53   253/100=2.53

253-100= 153 tons propellant using a 1:6 fuel/oxidizer mixture 153/7 = 22 tons LH_2

SiH_4/LOX rocket Isp 340 sec. Exhaust velocity = 3.332 km/sec $e^{(4.1/3.332)}$ = 3.42   342/100=3.42

342-100=242 tons propellant $SiH_4 + 2O_2 ==> SiO_2 + 2H_2O$
Si = 28 $2H_2$ = 4 $2O_2$=64

28+4+64=96   4/96 X 242 = 10.08 tons hydrogen

It is likely that hydrogen will be the "pinch point." Silicon and oxygen are abundant in Moon rocks, regolith, and C and S-type asteroids. There is enough solar wind implanted hydrogen on the Moon to provide water for early Moon bases but not enough to fuel rockets. There are huge amounts of hydrogen in polar ices but what will it cost to mine that ice? And do we want to waste such a precious resource that could be of immense value to future lunar civilization? It seems the smart thing to do would be to use less powerful silane and LOX to conserve hydrogen. This also eliminates nuclear dangers. Even greater efficiency might be had if silane is used as a carrier fluid for metal powder fuels (aluminum, magnesium, calcium and/or ferrosilicon) in bipropellant rockets.

A fleet of a thousand rocket ships with nuclear thermal motors would use 5,200,000 tons of hydrogen every year. With LH_2 and LOX propulsion they would use 15,300,000 tons of propellant overall but only 2,185,000 tons of hydrogen. With silane and LOX they would use a total of

24,200,000 tons of propellant but only one million tons of hydrogen. This will demand a lot of mining and material processing and transportation.

Annual Propellant and Hydrogen Demands for 1000 Ship Fleet

1000 ships X 100 flights (50 round trips) X 52 tons LH2 = 5,200,000 tons hydrogen

1000 X 100 X 153 = 15,300,000 tons propellant 1/7 of that is 2,185,000 tons hydrogen

1000 X 100 X 242 = 24,200,000 tons propellant 4/96 of that is 1,000,000 tons hydrogen

Carbonaceous chondrite asteroids contain 3 to 22% water.[71] If an asteroid that is 10% water is found then ninety million tons of asteroidal material must be dug and processed every year to provide one million tons of hydrogen for silane. If that material contains oxygen and silicon in percentages similar to the Moon then there will be more than enough oxygen and silicon for propellant. A quantity of rock several hundred meters wide would have to be mined. In ten years a whole mountain of an asteroid would be mined up. This task would be daunting.

Using silane for rocket fuel can cut hydrogen demand in half. If silane can be used as a carrier fluid for powdered metal based slurry fuels, hydrogen consumption can be reduced even more. Hydrogen could be piggybacked into LEO with payloads from Earth, obtained from lunar polar ices and mined from NEOs. Since lunar solar wind implanted volatiles are such a low density resource they will probably be reserved for life support and other uses but not rocket fuel. If helium 3 fusion becomes possible and economical in the future then large quantities of these volatiles will result from helium 3 mining on the Moon. There are millions of tons of ice in lunar polar craters. The exact amount and form it is in (sheets of ice, crystals mixed with regolith?) are unknown presently. Beyond the Moon and NEOs, hydrogen could come from ices of the moons of the outer planets. It could also come from the atmospheres of the Gas Giants. That's a resource humanity would have trouble exhausting! Rockets might be replaced by space elevators someday. Spacecraft could simply be flung off the ends of the tether with no propellant at all.

Making silane and oxygen would require processing regolith in SDR-AIS machines to get silicon and oxygen from loads of lunar regolith sent down to LEO. Powdered silicon would be mixed with powdered magnesium and heated up to form magnesium silicide. Hydrogen from the Moon or piggybacked up from Earth would be reacted with chlorine from Earth to make HCl. The magnesium silicide would then be reacted with HCl to form gaseous silane that would be piped off and liquefied. Solid magnesium chloride would remain. This would be electrolyzed to recover chlorine to make more HCl with new stocks of hydrogen and magnesium for reacting with more silicon.

MAKING SILANE

Hydrogen from Earth, Moon or Asteroids   Chlorine from Earth

Magnesium and Silicon from Moon or Asteroids

$2Mg + Si ==> Mg_2Si$ $2H_2 + 4Cl ==> 4 HCl$

$Mg_2Si + 4HCl ==> SiH_{4\,(g)} + 2 MgCl_{2\,(s)}$

Silane gas boils off and is liquefied. Magnesium chloride remains solid and is then put through electrolysis to recover and recycle Mg and Cl

---

Mars and Methane

There is plenty of carbon on Mars in the atmosphere and polar ice to make methane instead of silane. Methane is a bit more powerful than silane so it might be preferred. Only about 80% as much methane and LOX will be needed as silane and LOX, so this could lighten logistics and reduce rocket thrust requirements. Since the gravity of Mars is higher than the Moon's, more thrust will be called for. Extracting carbon from the atmosphere could be done with huge compressors. Hydrogen and oxygen could come from permafrost and polar water ices. More carbon could be obtained by mining and melting polar carbon dioxide ice. Making methane will be simpler than making silane. Carbon dioxide gas will be fed into Sabatier reactors with hydrogen to make water and carbon monoxide. The water will be condensed and electrolyzed to get hydrogen and oxygen and the hydrogen will be reacted with CO in a Sabatier reactor to make methane and water.

CH_4/LOX rocket Isp 380 seconds   Exhaust velocity = 3.724 km./sec.

$e^{(4.1/3.724)} = 3.007$ 300.7/100 = 3.007

 300.7-100 = 200.7 tons methane & LOX at 1:4 fuel/oxidizer ratio

$CH_4 + 2O_2 \rightarrow CO_2 + 2H_2O$

C = 12 H_4 = 4 $2O_2$ = 64

4/80 = 1/20   200.7/20 = 10.035 tons hydrogen

Methane is slightly better than silane for conserving hydrogen. It's probably easier to produce. Silane requires regolith mining and then separation of silicon from regolith. Then the silicon has to be reacted with magnesium to get magnesium silicide. This is then reacted with HCl. Hydrogen comes from mining solar wind implanted volatiles and polar ices on the Moon. This requires mining some large areas and working in super cold conditions. On Mars, you just have to dig up some permafrost laden regolith just about anywhere and roast out the water, and there is much more of it than any lunar resource. The hydrogen from the water is reacted with CO_2 pumped down from the atmosphere and fed into a network of pipes, chambers, water condensers, electrolyzers and Sabatier reactors. Methane, oxygen and maybe some extra hydrogen comes out and they are separated by fractional liquefication and stored. Hydrogen might be stored in solid media instead of liquid form. The whole methane and oxygen making process can be fully automated.

Fuel from the Outer Moons

The moons of the outer planets are covered with ice and the atmosphere of Titan is mostly methane and nitrogen. Ice could be melted and used as working fluid in solid core nuclear thermal rocket motors. Methane could also be liquefied and used as propellant in nuclear thermal rockets. There is no shortage of ice in the outer solar system, but the temperatures are so low that the ice will be super hard. Lasers or electron beams may be needed to cut blocks of ice out of the surfaces of outer planet moons. It might also be possible to drill holes into the ice and blast with oxyliquit explosives. The holes could be drilled with electrically heated molybdenum tipped heat probes. The oxyliquit explosives would consist of magnesium or aluminum tanks filled with a mixture of LOX and powdered magnesium or aluminum, depending on what's most available. This mixture would then be ignited with an electric spark and detonated. Oxyliquits could even be used on the Moon in place of nitrate based explosives.

Manned journeys to the outer planets will take years even with nuclear electric propulsion. Someday fusion drives will speed things up, but who can be sure about fusion? NEP and fusion will both demand hydrogen for reaction mass. If robots are sent to the outer moons first to mine ice and extract hydrogen it will be possible for manned ships to travel faster because they won't have to lug along enough reaction mass for return flight. Robots could also deploy habitat, extract oxygen from ice, and cover the habitat with blocks of ice for cosmic ray shielding. On Titan, the atmosphere might provide plenty of cosmic ray shielding.

Eventually, the Moon's resources of helium 3 will play out. The atmospheres of the giant planets also contain helium 3 and there's enough of it for millions of years. There is even more normal helium and hydrogen in the atmospheres of those planets along with some methane and ammonia. If it becomes more practical to mine the atmospheres of Jupiter, Saturn, Uranus and Neptune for these gases with balloon borne robotic factories or nuclear ram-jets that can "scoop" their atmospheres, rather than mine their moons for ice, a virtually limitless supply of light elements will result. Solar orbiting space settlements built from asteroids could buy hydrogen, helium, carbon and nitrogen from the atmosphere miners to supplement supplies tapped by mining water and tar from C-type asteroids. Starships running matter-antimatter engines could also use hydrogen for reaction mass. Hydrogen supplies will be limited only by human mining capabilities, not any natural shortage.

Planetary and National Defense

Planetary defense is a real concern. A small asteroid could destroy a major city. A large asteroid could cause a mass extinction. Detonating a nuclear weapon to deflect an asteroid might work, but is not popular. The best thing to do is to scan the sky with optical and radar telescopes to detect potentially hazardous asteroids and deflect them years ahead of time. It might be possible to use a spacecraft called a gravity tug. This has a huge mass that is propelled with rockets that need a lot of propellant into the vincinity of the asteroid. The mass and gravity of the tug pulls the asteroid off its course by just enough to keep it from impacting the Earth. This would work well on rubble pile asteroids. Solid asteroids could be deflected with a high speed, therefore high energy, impactor. This would all require substantial space industry to build the deflector spacecraft in high orbit, fuel them and let them do their work.

Lasers are interesting. What if it was possible to grow giant laser rods of crystal ruby or some other lasable material in the low gravity and clean vacuum of the Moon or a slowly rotating space station? Lasers could be used to deflect threatening asteroids. All this would require quite a bit of lunar and orbital industrial development. Lasers could also be used for national defense. A laser rod several feet in diameter and 60 feet long could be stowed in a Space Shuttle cargo bay. It would be grown on the Moon or in space and brought back to Earth by a revived and updated Space Shuttle. The laser could be used for anti-aircraft and anti-missile defenses on the ground and at sea. Hundreds of them might be built for national defense and that would require quite a bit of lunar and space infrastructure.

Ground based lasers using big artificial ruby rods and big xenon strobes powered by jet fuel fired gas turbine generators could be installed on the coasts for air defense of the nation. They could be based in Taiwan to fend off PRC aggression in the South China Sea and in Japan and South Korea to ward off missile threats from North Korea. Lasers in Israel and Saudi Arabia could shoot down enemy missiles launched by rebels and terrorists backed by Iran and other outlaw governments. Israel and Saudi Arabia have already come under attack with missiles launched by Hamas and other radical terrorist groups like the Yemen rebels.

If the laser rods can be made and if the project could be afforded, perhaps as part of a bootstrapping lunar mining base project, the limitation won't be energy to pump the lasers, but cooling. The rods heat up. They could be cooled with an inert gas like helium or argon that transfers heat via heat exchangers to CFCs or HFCs in a cooling system. Heavy refrigeration machinery and big waste heat radiators would be needed. In well-watered lands with lakes and rivers and at sea there would be plenty of water for cooling the waste heat radiators or heat exchangers. In space some huge space radiators would be needed and they would have to be shielded from the Sun. In the desert, large air cooled radiators would be needed unless the lasers are close to the coast where they could use seawater.

Ships could also use onboard seawater cooled systems to handle the waste heat. Even so there would probably be a limit to how much the cooling systems could handle before the laser would have to be shut down for awhile. There would be a limit to how much fuel the laser equipped ship could use to power and cool the laser, unless it was nuclear powered. American aircraft carriers and submarines are all nuclear powered these days and there were some nuclear cruisers. Ships the size of cruisers or destroyers could have lasers for protecting aircraft carriers. Nimitz class aircraft carriers have two nuclear reactors and 3.5 million gallons of jet fuel onboard. I don't know about the stats for Ford class carriers, but the fact is clear, those ships are floating loaded bombs. They cannot allow enemy vessels to get close enough to strike them with missiles, ballistic or cruise, or aircraft be they manned fighters or unmanned drones. Destroyers that cruise on efficient diesel power and use jet fuel powered gas turbines for combat speed could run generators to energize the laser with xenon flash lamps (strobes) that are so bright they can set steel wool on fire. The turbines could also operate the cooling water pumps and refrigeration machines that cool the laser rod crystal. Our aircraft carrier fleets provide air superiority over 80% of the globe's surface. With lasers that security could be maintained and improved upon. With 3000 men and women on board, we can never afford to lose an aircraft carrier in combat.

It might not be practical to swing the laser around like a mounted cannon. A reflector could be employed. Aiming could be handled by RADAR, LIDAR, modern computers, electronic controls and servomechanisms. Megawatt, even gigawatt, power levels would be required. Ultra-capacitor banks would store power from turbines and discharge into the strobes when firing the laser.

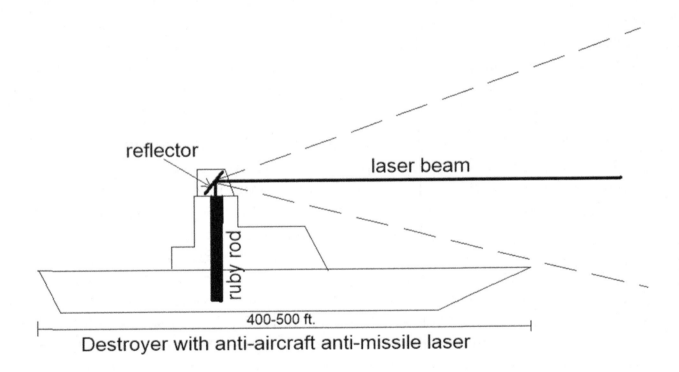

Fig. 11 Laser equipped ship for protecting aircraft carriers at sea.

On the Moon, anorthositic Highland regolith could be mined. The iron bearing minerals and meteoric iron fines could be removed with magnetic separators. Some electrostatic separation might also be used to get pure anorthosite. Even so, half the regolith grains might be rejected because they are agglutinates of more than one kind of mineral. The pure anorthosite would then be melted and quenched with liquid oxygen to form an amorphous glass that is then busted up with hammers and ground fine in rod and ball mills. The ground anorthosite would then be leached in sulfuric acid to get a precipitate of silicic acid and calcium sulfate and a solution of aluminum sulfate. The aluminum sulfate solution would then be filtered off and boiled down to recover the water and the sulfate would then be roasted at about 1000 C. to drive off the sulfur oxides and leave pure aluminum oxide behind. This would then be mixed with powdered chromium and melted in a large electrically heated crucible. A seed crystal would be placed in the melt and a large artificial ruby rod would be grown that does not fall apart under its own weight in the low G of the Moon or a space station. There will be no contamination by air in the vacuum.

It might also be possible to grow titanium sapphires by adding titanium instead of chromium to the aluminum oxide and using a Ti-sapphire seed crystal. This kind of laser emits light in the infrared range. Since the atmosphere absorbs IR this might not make a good weapon but it might be applied to fusion reactors.

If these lasers are possible at a reasonable price, they might also make laser fusion reactors possible. This would create a market for more laser rods made in space, helium 3 from the Moon, and possibly even fusion rocket engines for high-speed travel throughout the solar system. This may be largely speculation, but "what if?" American and allied security, energy and other problems could be resolved. Enemy air attack and rogue nations with ballistic missiles could be countered.

With its speed of light beam, the laser would be the ultimate anti-aircraft and anti-missile weapon. It could even neutralize the threat of hyper-sonic missiles. The laser would be used for defense more often than offense. Atmospheric absorption and diffraction will limit its range. Perhaps green, blue or ultraviolet lasers that cut through the atmosphere more aggressively could be developed. Multiple shot X-ray or even gamma ray lasers might also exist.

In the vacuum of space, lasers will not be effected by atmospheric gases. Their range would be limited only by the divergence of their beam over great distances. Space warships with lasers are not inconceivable. Law enforcement and military defenses to prevent smuggling, human trafficking and terrorism in space will become necessary someday.

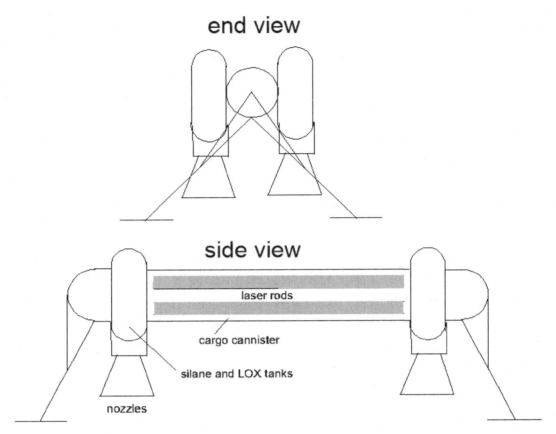

end view

side view

laser rods

cargo cannister

silane and LOX tanks

nozzles

Lunar surface to lunar orbit laser rod transport

Transporting the laser rods would be done with chemically propelled vessels that move the rods from the lunar surface to low lunar orbit. From there they would be propelled with solar electric ion drive tugs to LEO where they are loaded into an advanced space shuttle and hauled back to Edwards Air Force base surrounded by security teams.

Space Medicine

Astronauts are usually young, healthy and a cut above, but they still get sick despite vetting and pre-flight quarantine. In the future, space crews will be selected carefully and quarantined before working in space, but there will be large numbers of people that are older and not so healthy-tourists and workers with special knowledge or skills who aren't that health conscious. Perhaps their employers will ask them to lose weight, get in shape and quit smoking if they want the job. Space adventure might be just the motivation they need. Tourists might need a minimal degree of fitness to endure G-forces and weightlessness. A doctor's release may be required before taking a vacation in space. It might be wise to go to space camp and ride in a centrifuge and take a flight on the "vomit comet" before actually traveling in space. Settlers aiming for Mars better be healthy too. If they plan on having children, they are going to need medical facilities and pediatricians as well as OB-GYNs.

Some writers have claimed that Mars settlement will require large populations fast, and they have suggested that pregnant women should be sent to Mars so they can have babies soon after getting there. If this is true, then Mars settlers will need nurses, mid-wives, doctors especially obstetricians, hospitals with maternity wards, prenatal and neonatal ICUs, immunizations, infant formula, baby bottles and sterilizers, jars of baby food, diapers, cribs, baby clothes and later clothing for children of all ages, strollers, toys, schools therefore teachers, desks, books, computers, writing and drawing supplies, habitat for large families complete with multiple bathrooms, dinner tables and furniture, and finally 16 to 22 years or more to make those babies into productive citizens of Mars. That's a tall order.

In Earth orbit and on the Moon, it will be possible to rush sick people back to Earth when space hospitals can't treat them. For people going to Mars or beyond, this option won't exist. If they can reach Mars in 39 days instead of six months, it might be possible to stabilize their conditions with the limited medical facilities on board ship and get them to Mars before they die. On Mars they will need complete hospitals with operating rooms, surgical staff, labs, pharmacies and dental facilities for tooth extraction or root canals, etc. Ships to Titan or elsewhere in the solar system on years' long voyages will need complete hospitals too. Nobody wants to get stuck someplace where medical facilities are on the Third World level. At Antarctic bases medical care is provided to get people well enough to be moved by airplane to hospitals in New Zealand or Australia. Sick bays on aircraft carriers with crews of 3000 or more might be worth copying for space medical facilities. In space, hospitals will need the right stuff for handling every kind of health care challenge including decompression accidents and cancer due to radiation.

Logistics are challenging. There are about 24,000 medicines in use worldwide. The PDR lists about 2,400 of them. The WHO lists over 900 essential medicines. Besides medicine everything from surgical instruments to x-ray machines are needed. Clever engineers will have to figure out how to bootstrap all sorts of medical equipment to reduce import costs. Space farms will have to produce cotton for bandages. Nylon and PLA might also be produced for surgical thread.[72]

At first, medicines could be imported. In time, with growing populations in space, it will become more cost effective to make medicines in space, on the Moon and Mars. What kind of laboratory or chemical industry will be needed to make all these medicines and chemicals for diagnostic tests?

In earlier chapters, I discussed making chemicals from simple feedstocks, but my aim was for synthetic materials. Phenol from benzene, sodium hydroxide and acetic anhydride, all necessary to make aspirin can be produced. Phenol can also be used as an oral antiseptic. Aniline from benzene can be used to make antibiotic sulfa drugs which are still used today for urinary tract infections. To make thousands of drugs presents a challenge. Information about the processes to make medications can be stored in computers and skillful chemists and lab technicians could cook up almost anything needed given enough lab equipment and the right ingredients. Automation might also be applied.

Many drugs come from plants. The space farms might include some medicinal plants. Plant cell tissue culture might also be used. This might be faster and more productive than growing entire plants. Plant cells, fungi, molds and bacteria, some genetically programmed, could all be kept frozen and cultured to make various drugs or precursor chemicals that are then converted to actual medications. Genetically programmed animal cells like hamster ovarian cells might also be cultured. The use of living organisms to make medicines might be far more efficient than trying to synthesize thousands of organic chemicals in space laboratories with the simple feedstocks available. About 99% of today's medicines come from petrochemicals and there is no oil on the Moon or Mars. There are sources of hydrogen, water, carbon oxides, nitrogen, sulfur, sodium, phosphorus and various metals. These simple feedstocks would have to be converted to more complex organic chemicals for making drugs and that could be really complicated. If a plant or cell culture can produce a complex substance from just CO_2, water, sunlight and soil that can then be extracted and converted by a few chemical steps to an active medication, lunar and Martian pharmacists will be way ahead of the curve. This is called semi-synthesis.

This is illustrated by the story of the anti-cancer drug Taxol. It was first isolated from the bark of the Pacific Yew tree in 1962, but so little was available from these trees that they could never supply enough Taxol to treat the cancer cases in the U.S. In 1994, the first synthesis of the drug was achieved but it took 40 sequential chemical steps and was terribly inefficient. Finally, Robert Holton, a professor at Florida State University, came up with a four-step process that made Taxol from a substance called 10-deacetylbaccatin extracted from the needles of the common English Yew shrub.[73] This process is far more productive besides being simpler.

Perhaps cancer patients could be sent from the Moon back to Earth, unless they were born and raised on the Moon, in which case they might never be able to stand up to the gravity of Earth. Maybe they could adapt to the gravity of Mars and Mercury or some of moons of the outer planets, but they might never come to Earth unless medical science finds a way to prevent bone and muscle atrophy in low G and insure natural development of children born on the Moon so that they will be strong enough to stand up to 1 G. If not, then cancer drugs would have to be shipped to the Moon. On Mars, even if Martians could return to a 1 G environment, and even if they had nuclear electric ships that could reach Earth in 39 days, they might have to wait two years for a launch window. Mars settlers will be wise to take a large stock of medicines along with themselves and some

English Yew shrub seeds, cell cultures or cuttings too, in addition to other plants, bacteria and molds like the ones used to make Penicillin. With abundant CO_2 and water, compared to the Moon, it should be possible to create a large organic chemical industry on Mars. The Martians might make money selling and shipping medicines to lunar and free space settlements since it takes less energy to travel from Mars to many other locations in space than it does from Earth.

At: https://www.rain-tree.com/plantdrugs.htm there is a list of 120 plants and the drugs derived from them. Perhaps these plants or cell cultures could be cultivated. Here are some of them:

Drug/Chemical	Action/Clinical Use	Plant Source
Acetyldigoxin	Cardiotonic	Digitalis lanata
Aesculetin	Anti-dysentery	Frazinus rhychophylla
Agrimophol	Anthelmintic	Agrimonia supatoria
Anabesine	Skeletal muscle relaxant	Anabasis sphylla
Asiaticoside	Vulnerary	Centella asiatica
Atropine	Anticholinergic	Atropa belladonna
Benzyl benzoate	Scabicide	Several plants
Berberine	Bacillary dysentery	Berberis vulgaris
Bergenin	Antitussive	Ardisia japonica
Betulinic acid	Anticancerous	Betula alba
Caffeine	CNS stimulant	Camellia sinensis
Camphor	Rubefacient	Cinnamomum camphora
Camptothecin	Anticancerous	**Camptotheca acuminata**
(+)-Catechin	Haemostatic	Potentilla fragarioides
Chymopapain	Proteolytic, mucolytic	Carica papaya
Cocaine	Local anaesthetic	Erythroxylum coca

Codeine	Analgesic, antitussive	Papaver somniferum
Colchiceine amide	Antitumor agent	Colchicum autumnale
Colchicine	Antitumor agent, anti-gout	Colchicum autumnale
Curcumin	Choleretic	Curcuma longa
Cynarin	Choleretic	Cynara scolymus
Demecolcine	Antitumor agent	Colchicum autumnale
Deserpidine	Antihypertensive, tranquillizer	Rauvolfia canescens
Deslanoside	Cardiotonic	Digitalis lanata
L-Dopa	Anti-parkinsonism	Mucuna sp
Digitalin	Cardiotonic	Digitalis purpurea
Digitoxin	Cardiotonic	Digitalis purpurea
Digoxin	Cardiotonic	Digitalis purpurea
Emetine	Amoebicide, emetic	Cephaelis ipecacuanha
Ephedrine	Sympathomimetic, antihistamine	Ephedra sinica
Etoposide	Antitumor agent	Podophyllum peltatum
Galanthamine	Cholinesterase inhibitor	Lycoris squamigera
Glasiovine	Antidepressant	Octea glaziovii
Glycyrrhizin	Sweetener, Addison's disease	Glycyrrhiza glabra
Hemsleyadin	Bacillary dysentery	Hemsleya amabilis
Hesperidin	Capillary fragility	Citrus species
Hydrastine	Hemostatic, astringent	Hydrastis canadensis
Hyoscyamine	Anticholinergic	Hyoscyamus niger
Irinotecan	Anticancer, antitumor agent	Camptotheca acuminata
Kaibic acud	Ascaricide	Digenea simplex
Kawain	Tranquillizer	Piper methysticum
Kheltin	Bronchodilator	Ammi visaga
Lanatosides A, B, C	Cardiotonic	Digitalis lanata
Lapachol	Anticancer, antitumor	Tabebuia sp.
Menthol	Rubefacient	Mentha species

Methyl salicylate	Rubefacient	Gaultheria procumbens
Monocrotaline	Antitumor agent (topical)	Crotalaria sessiliflora
Morphine	Analgesic	Papaver somniferum
Nicotine	Insecticide	Nicotiana tabacum
Noscapine	Antitussive	Papaver somniferum
Ouabain	Cardiotonic	Strophanthus gratus
Pachycarpine	Oxytocic	Sophora pschycarpa
Papavarine	Smooth muscle relaxant	Papaver somniferum
Physostigmine	Cholinesterase Inhibitor	Physostigma venenosum
Picrotoxin	Analeptic	Anamirta cocculus
Pilocarpine	Parasympathomimetic	Pilocarpus jaborandi
Pinitol	Expectorant	Several plants
Podophyllotoxin	Antitumor anticancer agent	Podophyllum peltatum
Protoveratrines A, B	Antihypertensives	Veratrum album
Pseudoephredrine*	Sympathomimetic	Ephedra sinica
Pseudoephedrine, nor-	Sympathomimetic	Ephedra sinica
Quinidine	Antiarrhythmic	Cinchona ledgeriana
Quinine	Antimalarial, antipyretic	Cinchona ledgeriana
Rescinnamine	Antihypertensive, tranquillizer	Rauvolfia serpentina
Reserpine	Antihypertensive, tranquillizer	Rauvolfia serpentina
Rhomitoxin	Antihypertensive, tranquillizer	Rhododendron molle
Rotundine	Analagesic, sedative, traquillizer	Stephania sinica
Rutin	Capillary fragility	Citrus species
Salicin	Analgesic	Salix alba
Scopolamine	Sedative	Datura species
Sennosides A, B	Laxative	Cassia species
Silymarin	Antihepatotoxic	Silybum marianum
Sparteine	Oxytocic	Cytisus scoparius
Taxol	Antitumor agent	Taxus brevifolia

Teniposide	Antitumor agent	**Podophyllum peltatum**
a-Tetrahydrocannabinol(THC)	Antiemetic, decrease occular tension	**Cannabis sativa**
Tetrahydropalmatine	Analgesic, sedative, traquillizer	Corydalis ambigua
Tetrandrine	Antihypertensive	Stephania tetrandra
Theobromine	Diuretic, vasodilator	**Theobroma cacao**
Theophylline	Diuretic, brochodilator	**Theobroma cacao and others**
Thymol	Antifungal (topical)	Thymus vulgaris
Topotecan	Antitumor, anticancer agent	**Camptotheca acuminata**
Tubocurarine	Skeletal muscle relaxant	**Chondodendron tomentosum**
Valapotriates	Sedative	Valeriana officinalis
Vasicine	Cerebral stimulant	**Vinca minor**
Vinblastine	Antitumor, Antileukemic agent	**Catharanthus roseus**
Vincristine	Antitumor, Antileukemic agent	**Catharanthus roseus**

Some of these drugs might serve as precursors to better medicines. Many other plants that contain precursors if not actual drugs could also be considered. Also of interest, some plants contain more than one drug. For instance, Papaver somniferum, the opium poppy, contains several drugs. Digitalis contains several drugs for strengthening a failing heart. Rauvolfia serpentina, Cinchona ledgeriana, Ephedra sinica and Catharanthus roseus each contain more than one drug.

A list of chemicals found in medicinal herbs and plants that are believed to be active ingredients can be found here: https://www.herbal-supplement-resource.com/phytochemicals-herbs.html A list of phytochemicals found in food can be found here: https://en.wikipedia.org/wiki/List_of_phytochemicals_in_food

Many of these might be of value for the semi-synthesis of life saving medicines. Even if there are processes that are more expensive than total synthesis from petrochemicals, they would still be worth using in the outer space environment where of course, there are no cheap petrochemicals.

A research team consisting of doctors, botanists, pharmacists, pharmaceutical company executives, organic chemists and chemical engineers could be assembled by NASA and do millions of dollars' worth of research into the challenge of producing medications in space. Scientists today are studying the production of medicines from plants, fungi, molds and bacteria since this is much "greener" than making drugs from petrochemicals in a world where someday oil will be depleted. When we settle the Moon and other places in space, these green alternatives might be well developed by Earthly industry.

Pill bottles and reusable syringes might be made of glass, but there will still be a need for plastics for IV hoses, surgical gloves and such. If blood and IV solutions are to be stored in glass bottles and glass syringes are to be used, we better have autoclaves to sterilize them for reuse. We will have to look at the way things were done before the era of cheap disposable plastics.

Although NASA has and could do more research into space medicine, private industry will have to meet the challenge headlong of providing health care to large numbers of people in space. We can expect familiar stores like Walgreen's and CVS on the high frontier and name brands like Johnson & Johnson and Bayer. The price of health care in space will probably be higher than it is on Earth, given the costs of establishing hospitals, dental offices, medical supply companies and drug labs in addition to the high cost of necessary imports.

Skilled artisans could blow glass from abundant lunar silicon dioxide to make laboratory and medical equipment, presuming it's cheaper to send up human workers than it is to import things. Simple glass bottles could be blown by machines in large numbers. Cotton farming and a small textile industry will be needed with workers to weave and sew bandages, sheets, pajamas, scrubs, etc. Bed frames might be made of metal and basalt with mattresses made of basalt fiber cloth stuffed with basalt fibers. Plaster for casts should be available as a by product of sulfuric acid leaching to get silicon dioxide from regolith. Pure oxygen will be plentiful as it is a by product of metal extraction. Oxygen for breathing will be highly purified while oxygen for rocket propellant won't have to be so clean. Nitrogen is not very abundant on the Moon but there should be enough to make nitrous oxide anesthetic with electric arcs. The nitrous could be recovered for reuse after cleaning with a closed circuit breathing device. Steam, ethanol, hydrogen peroxide and UV light could be used to sanitize things including entire operating rooms.

Experience delivering health care in orbit and on the Moon could later be applied to Mars settlement and beyond. It would behoove Martians and other space settlers to figure out how to provide health care in a situation with very little industrial development, no petrochemicals and no possibility of rapid return to Earth for treatment.

Only a small percentage of the work force would have to be devoted to medical treatment and making pharmaceuticals. Many of them might do two jobs. For instance, a nurse could also be a pharmacist and a radiology technician could also work in the lab. Space farms might be tended by robots and that would free up a lot of labor. The people delivering health care will have to be paid and the people receiving care will have to foot the bills. Space crews will need medical insurance and acceptable currency in terrestrial bank accounts. All the paperwork could be handled by computers and by telecommunication radio or laser links with Earth. Large numbers of administrators will not be needed in space, at least not until populations have grown really large and every kind of service is needed.

Hygienic practices cannot be ignored. Soap will be easy to make from animal or vegetable fats. Toothbrushes and other sundry items will be imported until polymer and razor blade industries exist in space, on the Moon and Mars. Salt and baking soda might be used instead of costly imported toothpaste. People will go into space to work for months and years. Some people will go there and stay for the rest of their lives. The inexpensive common-place day to day items we take for granted on Earth will also be needed in space. Merchants might import things and sell them with mark-up, but they could probably make more sales and even better profits if they can make their wares on-site and sell them at a lower price.

Spacesuits

Spacesuits cost millions of dollars. They require many synthetic polymers. There is no oil, coal or gas on the Moon or Mars but there are sources of hydrogen and carbon oxides. I've written about making some simple chemicals from H and CO, but to make a spacesuit some real complex chemistry is involved. To make a spacesuit we also need complex electronics, lithium hydroxide to absorb CO_2, etc. Some spacesuit components might be made in space, on the Moon or Mars, and some could be imported from Earth until mining and industry off-Earth can provide them.

Without space suits, there will be no space exploration. We will probably get our space suits from Mother Earth for a long time. Eventually we will mine solar wind implanted volatiles, lunar polar ices, near Earth objects and on Mars there is CO_2 in the atmosphere and water ice. These will make it possible to synthesize polymers.

At: http://www.madehow.com/Volume-5/Spacesuit.html , we read that: *Numerous raw materials are used for constructing a spacesuit. Fabric materials include a variety of different synthetic polymers. The innermost layer is made up of a Nylon tricot material. Another layer is composed of spandex, an elastic wearable polymer. There is also a layer of urethane-coated nylon, which is involved in pressurization. Dacron—a type of polyester—is used for a pressure-restraining layer. Other synthetic fabrics used include Neoprene that is a type of sponge rubber, aluminized Mylar, Gortex, Kevlar, and Nomex.*

Beyond synthetic fibers other raw materials have important roles. Fiberglass is the primary material for the hard upper torso segment. Lithium hydroxide is used in making the filter which removes carbon dioxide and water vapor during a space walk. A silver zinc blend comprises the battery that powers the suit. Plastic tubing is woven into the fabric to transport cooling water throughout the suit. A polycarbonate material is used for constructing the shell of the helmet. Various other components are used to make up the electronic circuitry and suit controls.

So we need several polymers—Nylon, Spandex, urethane, Dacron, Neoprene, Mylar, Gortex, Kevlar and Nomex. Polycarbonate is also needed to make transparent space helmets.

Polycarbonate

Polycarbonate is a strong, impact resistant plastic used for space helmets. It is good at 115-130 C. (239-266 F.) down to -40 C. (-40 F.) and it is a good blocker of UV light. It is made from phenol which will come from benzene made on the Moon or Mars from acetylene or obtained from polar ice.

Phenol is made by reacting benzene with propylene by compressing them together to a pressure of 30 atmospheres at 250 °C in presence of phosphoric acid. This forms cumene which oxidizes to cumene hydroperoxide which is then hydrolyzed in an acidic medium to form phenol and acetone. Propylene will come from the reaction of hydrogen and carbon monoxide on the Moon and Mars.

$$6 H_2 + 3 CO \rightarrow C_3H_6 + 3 H_2O$$

As an aside, phenol is also reacted with formaldehyde to make Bakelite, a hard, scratch resistant, insulating plastic. Phenolic resins continue to be used for a wide variety of applications, such as moulding powders, laminating resins, adhesives, binders, surface coatings and impregnants.

Polycarbonate can be made by reacting bisphenol-A (BPA) with phosgene. Phosgene is toxic and has been used as a chemical warfare argent. It is also possible to make polycarbonate by reacting BPA with diphenyl carbonate $(C_6H_5O)_2CO$ made by reacting phenol with carbon monoxide.

$$2 C_6H_5OH + CO + [O] \rightarrow (C_6H_5O)_2CO + H_2O$$

Phenol   **Diphenyl carbonate**

This is much "greener" and will be much safer on the Moon or Mars where accidental contamination of habitat atmosphere could be catastrophic.

$$(HOC_6H_4)_2C(CH_3)_2 + (C_6H_5O)_2CO \rightarrow 1/n [OC(OC_6H_4)_2C(CH_3)_2]_n + 2 C_6H_5OH$$

BPA   **diphenyl carbonate**   **polycarbonate**   **phenol**

In the process of making polycarbonate we will have extra phenol remaining that could be used to make more diphenyl carbonate.

So how do we make BPA? From Wikipedia we read: *[BPA] is synthesized by the condensation of acetone (hence the suffix A in the name) with two [molar] equivalents of phenol. The reaction is catalyzed by a strong acid, such as hydrochloric acid (HCl) or a sulfonated polystyrene resin. Industrially, a large excess of phenol is used to ensure full condensation; the product mixture of the cumene process (acetone and phenol) may also be used as starting material:*

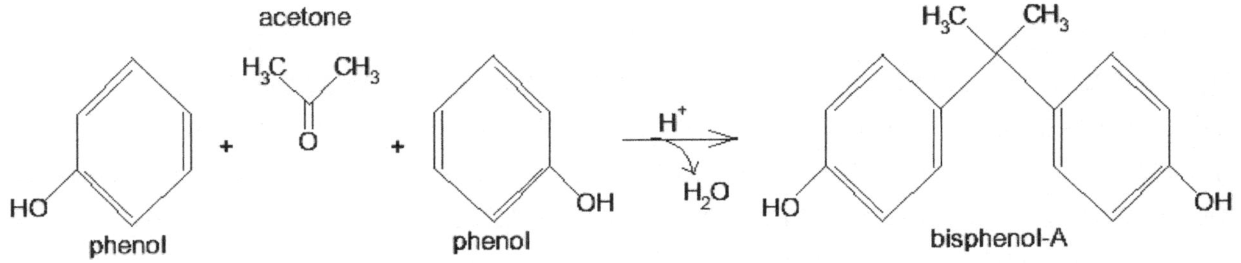

As we can see, two mols of phenol are reacted with one mol of acetone to make one mol of BPA. In the cumene process one mol of benzene combines with one mol of propylene to form one mol of phenol and one mol of acetone. Thus, we will need one mol of phenol and one half mol of acetone to make one half mol of BPA. It seems we will have more acetone than phenol for BPA.

Nylon

Besides spacesuits, Nylons (also called polyamides) have many more everyday clothing uses. The Nylon making process is not simple. Benzene, ordinarily extracted from crude oil, is needed. On the Moon or Mars, benzene can be made by passing acetylene through a red hot iron pipe at about 600 C. Acetylene production was discussed in earlier chapters. Benzene is the main raw material for the industrial production of Nylon 6 and Nylon 66. Benzene is converted to cyclohexane by reacting it with hydrogen in the presence of a Raney-nickel catalyst.[74] Cyclohexane is a precursor to both caprolactam used to make Nylon 6 and adipic acid used to make Nylon 66.[75] Cyclohexane is converted to cyclohexanone and cyclohexanol by oxidation and the use of cobalt catalysts.[76] Cobalt can be extracted from meteoric iron fines on the Moon. The cyclohexanone and cyclohexanol mixture is reacted with nitric acid to form adipic acid. Cyclohexanone can also be converted to cyclohexanone oxime which is converted to caprolactam using a sulfuric acid catalyst.

Some Nylon monomers can be extracted from Castor oil. Sebacic acid is used to make Nylon 510.[77] Oil from the Castor bean is also a good machine lubricant.

Spandex

Spandex is made from two pre-polymers. One is a macroglycol while the other is a diisocyanate. The macro-glycol can be a polyester, polyether, polycarbonate, polycaprolactone or some combination of these. The other prepolymer used to produce spandex is a polymeric diisocyanate. [78] Isocyanates contain a R-N=C=O group and diisocyanates have one on each end.

According to Wikipedia, isocyanates are produced from amines by phosgenation, in other words, treating with phosgene: [79]

$$RNH_2 + COCl_2 \rightarrow RNCO + 2\,HCl$$

amine   phosgene   isocyanate

Making amines may require ammonia (NH_3). Ammonia can be made by reacting hydrogen and nitrogen in the presence of an iron catalyst at high temperatures and pressures. This is called the Haber process.

Chlorine is necessary and this element is rare on the Moon. We could get it by sulfuric acid leaching of the mineral apatite. Otherwise it would have to be imported. Chlorine seems to be fairly abundant on Mars in the form of perchlorates in the regolith. Since the reaction above produces HCl it might be possible to recycle the chlorine to make more phosgene.

Phosgene is made by pumping carbon monoxide and chlorine gases through a catalytic bed of activated carbon. [80] It's easy to make, but do we want anything to do with this stuff? It was used as poison gas during WW1. It causes pulmonary edema, swelling in the lungs. Working with carbon monoxide and chlorine is bad enough in sealed habitat. Phosgene could be even worse. If these substances are to be used in space they will have to be used in modules separate from human and farm habitat and preferably be handled by robots. Otherwise, we have to find other ways to make isocyanates or use materials other than Spandex for our spacesuits.

Polyurethane

Polyurethane is not so simple either. Polyurethane polymers are traditionally and most commonly formed by reacting a di- or triisocyanate with a polyol. Isocyanates are produced via phosgene as discussed above and they are needed for spandex and polyurethane. Finding another way to make isocyanates without phosgene or using a material other than polyurethane is called for. If polyurethane is used, it can be made by reacting a diisocyanate with ethylene glycol, a diol. [81]

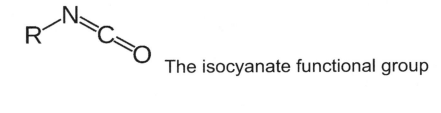
The isocyanate functional group

A commonly used diisocyanate is methylene diphenyl diisocyanate or MDI. Benzene is reacted with nitric and sulfuric acids to make nitrobenzene which is then hydrogenated to make aniline.[82] Aniline and formaldehyde are reacted in the presence of an HCl catalyst to make methylenedianiline or MDA. This MDA is reacted with phosgene to make MDI.[83] All these raw materials can be produced on the Moon or Mars.

Dacron

Dacron is a thermoplastic polymer material and a member of the polyester family. Polyester is the given name to a group of materials, whereas Dacron is a brand name of polyethylene terephthalate (PET). This is used as a pressure restraining layer in spacesuits so it's a very important material. Like Nylons, it also has everyday clothing applications. It can be produced by reacting ethylene glycol, $C_2H_4(OH)_2$, with dimethylterephthalate (DMT) or terephthalic acid.[84]

How do we get ethylene glycol? Ethylene glycol is made by reacting ethylene oxide with water and ethylene oxide is made by oxidizing ethylene in the presence of a silver catalyst. Ethylene, C_2H_4, can be made by combining hydrogen and carbon monoxide in the right proportions in the presence of a catalyst.

$$2CO + 4H_2 \rightarrow C_2H_4 + 2H_2O$$

In the DMT process, this chemical and $C_2H_4(OH)_2$ are reacted at 150-200 °C. Methanol and excess ethylene glycol are distilled off at reduced pressure. In the terephthalic acid process, ethylene glycol and terephthalic acid are reacted at 2.7-5.5 atmospheres of pressure and temperatures of 220-260° C. Sounds rather simple but probably involves a space chemical engineer's nightmare of pipes, valves, reactors, pumps, compressors, heating units and the challenging task of figuring out how to make all this in the austere environments of the Moon, Mars or free space. Obviously, production of synthetic materials like Dacron will require the development of raw materials sources first, like the production of carbon and hydrogen from ices, and the extraction of metals from regolith to make chemical equipment. That will also require molds, machine tools, rolling mills, extruders, presses, 3D printers, etc. Many of these things will be made off-Earth and many will be rocketed up from Earth. This is one reason why spacesuits will be made on Earth and shipped into space for a long time. Even after polymer production is going on the Moon or Mars, electronic components that can only be made in multi-billion dollar semiconductor fabrication plants will probably be shipped up from Earth. Fortunately, these electronic "chips" won't be very bulky and they won't weigh much so the cost of rocketing them into space won't be exorbitant, considering their value. Many imports could be launched affordably with Falcon Heavy rockets. If the Space X Super Heavy and Starship meets up to expectations, the cost of importing things from Earth will be even lower. Blue Origin might enter the competition too.

The next question is, how do we get DMT or terephthalic acid? That was discussed in the chapter, "Benzene and Derivatives."

Neoprene

Neoprene is also used in spacesuits. It is a form of synthetic rubber that resists degradation and is good for gaskets, hoses and corrosion resisting coatings. How do we make Neoprene with just simple feedstocks like hydrogen, CO, CO_2 and N and chemicals made from them???

It is made by the polymerization of chloroprene, hence it is also called polychloroprene. Polymerization of chloroprene is initiated with potassium persulfate and it is cross linked with metal oxides and thioureas. [85]

Chloroprene can be made in a couple of ways. The old way involves acetylene which can be produced on the Moon or Mars, but it is energy intensive and produces an explosive intermediate. From Wikipedia we read that chloroprene can also be produced by: *Chloroprene is produced in three steps from 1,3-butadiene: (i) chlorination, (ii) isomerization of part of the product stream, and (iii) dehydrochlorination of 3,4-dichlorobut-1-ene.* [86]

Butadiene is derived by the steam cracking of petroleum. It can also be made from ethanol by heating it to 400-450° C. over metal oxide catalysts.[87] Ethanol can be made by hydrating ethylene or by fermentation. Which process will be more efficient in space??? With butadiene from ethanol and chlorine the process can be started. Dehydrochlorination will require strong bases or thermal cracking. Potassium persulfate, metal oxides and thioureas can be produced with elements available on the Moon and Mars.

Gortex

Gortex is a form of stretched PTFE, also known as Teflon. Flourine is needed to make this substance and there is very little of this element on the Moon. Imports will be required, or fluorine could be extracted from lunar apatite concentrated by electrostatic separators. Sulfuric acid could extract HF, HCl and H_3PO_4 from apatite.

Kevlar and Nomex

Kevlar and Nomex are strong heat resistant aramids.

Kevlar is made by: Kevlar is made by the condensation reaction of para-phenylenediamine and terephthaloyl chloride. Hydrochloric acid is a by-product.

Para-phenylenediamine can be made from aniline which can be made from benzene. Terephthaloyl chloride can be made by chlorination of dimethyl terephthalate (DMT). This one of the chemicals needed to make polyester (PET), so once again polyester should be made first.

Nomex: Nomex is produced from the reaction of meta-pheylenediamine and isophthaloyl chloride. The *m*-phenylenediamine is produced by hydrogenation of 1,3-dinitrobenzene. The dinitrobenzene is prepared by dinitration of benzene.

Nitration requires nitric acid that can be made from nitrogen obtained by solar wind implanted volatiles mining and possibly from ammonia in polar ices. Benzene is easy to make as described above.

Isophthalic acid is produced on the billion kilogram per year scale by oxidizing meta-xylene with oxygen and a cobalt-manganese catalyst. Meta-xylene can be made from toluene made from benzene and possibly toluene from polar ices. Cobalt exists in meteoric iron fines and manganese is present in lunar regolith.

Fiberglass

Hard upper torso sections of spacesuits are made from fiberglass. Producing glass fibers on the Moon or Mars or in space from asteroid minerals will not be too complicated. Silicon dioxide and oxides of calcium, sodium, potassium, magnesium and aluminum added to the SiO_2 to lower the melting point and improve the workability of the glass are abundant in regolith and rocks. Dr. Geoffrey Landis has described the production of aluminosilicate glass on the Moon. This glass formulation melts at 1130°C. That's higher than the m.p. of soda-lime glass (860°C.) but much lower than the 1710°C. m.p. of unworkable silicon dioxide or pure silica glass. [88]

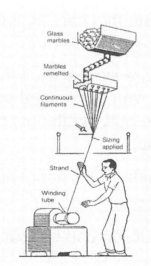

Figure 8

Glass Drawing
When silicate glasses are melted, they are viscous and thus can readily be drawn by special machines into fibers or rods or tubes. Glass fiber textiles and mats, which are commonly used terrestrially as thermal and electrical insulators, could be used as construction materials in a space facility.
From Shand 1958. p. 385.

NASA

For fiberglass, glass filaments are bound with a thermosetting polymer like epoxy, polyester resin or vinyl ester resin.[89] It should be possible to make these given the resources of lunar polar ices, lunar solar wind implanted volatiles, Martian sources of hydrogen, carbon, chlorine and nitrogen, and hydrocarbons from asteroids. The chemistry of these polymer matrix substances is rather complex and won't be discussed here.

Non-polymer Elements

Lithium hydroxide is needed for carbon dioxide removal from spacesuit breathing gas. It absorbs CO_2 and forms lithium carbonate which can be heated and decomposed to lithium hydroxide and CO_2 that is released into habitat atmosphere where it is processed by algae, crops and other green plants in the habitat life support system. Lithium is almost non-existent on the Moon. If there are lithium bearing minerals on Mars they have yet to be discovered. This element will have to be shipped into space and carefully recycled. Lithium batteries for spacesuit systems power might be used instead of silver-zinc batteries.

Conclusions

Castor bean oil might be used in the production of Nylon 510. Caraway oil might be used in polyester production. Could we create a genetically modified algae or yeast to produce these biological oils??? Ethanol for Neoprene production might be made by fermentation.

Neoprene can be made from acetylene which is easy to produce, but that process forms an unstable intermediate that can explode, so we really don't want to do things that way.

Spandex and Polyurethane both require isocyanates that are made using phosgene, a toxic chemical that has even been used as poison gas in warfare. It would be preferable to use other materials or a production process that doesn't require phosgene.

We must also wonder about using spider silk from genetically modified yeast for making spacesuits.

An in depth description of nylon production can be found here:
https://www.researchgate.net/publication/226332671_Industrial_Catalytic_Aspects_of_the_Synthesis_of_Monomers_for_Nylon_Production

Beyond the Moon and Mars

Humans and their domesticated plants and animals will go beyond the Moon and Mars someday. They will build settlements in orbit around various planets and in solar orbit. These have been called O'Neill habitat or space colonies. The word "colony" has a bad connotation especially in countries that were once conquered and colonized by the Europeans. Settlement is the preferred term. A colony is planted to support the mother country that rules it. This might happen; however, it's entirely likely that most space settlements will be privately owned and independent from Earthly governments. The goal of space settlement is not to exploit the resources of outer space for any government back on Earth, but to extend the domain of the human species. Space settlement might help civilization on the home planet thrive with energy resources like space solar and helium 3. It can also make use of space resources like metals, oxygen, light elements and basalt for a fantastic space travel industry that opens up the cosmos for anyone who really wants to visit outer space, other planets, or even permanently settle in space. Settlers will not be limited to planetary surfaces and underground habitations; they can also build settlements in space that rotate to produce 1 G with interiors filled with trees, gardens, farms, parks and homes.

How will that happen? At first materials will come from the Moon. Later, there will be materials from asteroids. In Mars orbit, materials will be launched up from the surface of Mars by rocket or mass drivers atop some of the great shield volcanoes, and materials will be mined on Deimos and Phobos. Asteroids will be the biggest source of materials for space settlement construction. Stony asteroids contain oxygen, silicon, iron, magnesium and lesser amounts of aluminum and calcium. Metallic asteroids are mostly iron, nickel, lesser amounts of cobalt and germanium, and platinum group metals. Carbonaceous asteroids contain water and hydrocarbons. Space settlements don't have to consist of giant aluminum cylinders or spheres. There are vast resources of iron, nickel and hydrocarbons in the asteroids that can be used to make high strength steel for settlement construction. Glass fiber cables made from asteroid rock can be used to pre-stress the giant steel cylinders or spheres so that internal pressure and rotation produce less hoop stress on the structures. The inner sides of the steel hulls will be coated to prevent rusting out. A thick layer of regolith inside will shield inhabitants from space radiations and allow the planting of crops and trees. Much food will be produced in vertical hydroponic farms. Solar energy will power the settlements, even in the outer solar system where giant reflectors will be used to collect sunshine. A very pleasant interior environment will be created. Homes will be made of glass bricks, metal and rock.

The raw materials are there and no wildlife or people are going to be pushed off their land, so whoever gets there first can take those metals and stone and build things. There are so many asteroids in the solar system that it is unlikely, but not impossible, for anyone to come into conflict over asteroid ownership. Resolution of such conflicts will be up to the United Federation of Worlds and Space Fleet. Even so, mining millions, even billions, of tons of materials from asteroids, even in microgravity, and processing them into metal alloys and assembling miles wide cylinders or spheres seems impossible. It might take decades or centuries to build these things. The only way to do the job is to use AI robots. One human worker might supervise a swarm of robots. Armies of human construction workers and welders in space would require habitat, food, water, oxygen and more. They probably wouldn't be able to work as fast as AI robot armies either. The task of assembling the shell of the space settlement will probably involve a lot of repetition and robots are better at that than humans. Once the shell is built and filled with oxygen and nitrogen along with some soil and water, the future inhabitants can go inside and plant crops, build houses and make almost everything else they want.

How will anyone pay for these settlements? They will buy robots and let the robots replicate until they have the swarms needed to do the work. Where will they get the money to buy the robots? And how long will they have to wait to finish the shell and move in? I can only see this happening for humans with extended life spans through genetic engineering. If they can live for centuries, they can work, save up money, invest, go into business for themselves and amass fortunes. If it takes 50 years or longer to build a space settlement in which they plan to build their dream homes and establish model communities beyond the jurisdiction of any planetary government, it seems that would be acceptable to people who can live 300 years or more. They would not be the sole owners of the settlement. Anywhere from 10,000 to a million people would share the settlement and it might take from 100 to 200 years to earn enough money to buy in. There would be private property and there would be public parks, roads, forests and infrastructure for water, sewerage and electricity. A small democratically elected government would be established to oversee all the public property and enforce laws. Anarchy in space is probably unworkable.

These future humans would not breed out of control and swell the population faster than any swarm of AI robots can build settlements to house them. Mastery of human reproductive biology and the conquest of all disease and deformity could make it possible to breed when one was about 100 years old and still youthful. There would only be three or four generations alive at any time. We would not climb so far just to reproduce like cockroaches and destroy ourselves in a swamp of human flesh and filth. Instead, we will live for higher purposes. The challenge of space settlement is certainly a worthwhile pursuit for people reaching for the stars. Human brainpower might be improved by genetic engineering. It will also be possible to accrue a vast amount of education, knowledge and work experience for people who have centuries rather than a few short years followed by entry into the work force, marriage, and retirement a few decades later followed by stagnation and death. Life extension will allow humans to learn and evolve into wiser, more intelligent creatures.

Resources of metal, stone, glass and hydrocarbons are abundant in the asteroids of the solar system. There are also hydrocarbons on Titan and inexhaustible amounts of hydrogen, helium including helium 3, methane and ammonia in the atmospheres of the Gas Giants and Ice Giants. There seem to be enormous quantities of ice and light elements in the trans-Neptunian objects of the Kuiper Belt and comets of the distant Oort Cloud. We can only hope that nearby star systems are as rich as ours is.

Space settlements probably won't be large enough to plant forests for wood and paper. Bamboo and hemp will be popular for paper products. Most things will be made of metal, stone, glass and ceramics. Even though there are plenty of hydrocarbons from C-type asteroids, Titan and the atmospheres of the giant planets, they won't come cheap. Plastics and other synthetic materials would be rigorously recycled. Space settlement interiors will have no room for trash dumps. Lessons in recycling will be learned very well back on Earth, or civilization will collapse before humanity reaches the High Frontier. Sewage will not be dumped in ponds and streams inside the settlements. It will be mixed with other wastes and subjected to biological degradation by yeast and aerobic bacteria like the kind in compost to create nutrient solution for hydroponic farms and algae tanks. Inside the settlements, the environment will be controlled and mild temperatures will last all year round, so multiple harvests will be had every 365 Earth days. There won't be any crop failures due to drought, flooding or storms.

There won't be any smokestack industries in the settlements. There might be electric furnaces for melting crushed rock and regolith to make bricks, blocks, glass, ceramic slabs, pipes for plumbing, etc. Any work with dangerous chemicals will be done outside in the vacuum or in nearby factory space stations. Human workers will wear spacesuits or haz-mat suits or the work with toxic substances will be done by robots. Bio-technology could be so advanced that any medicine can be produced by genetically programmed bacteria, yeast, plant or animal cell cultures without the dangers of working with poisonous chemicals.

Synthetic rubber, plastics, Nylons, paint, ink, dyes and other products made from hydrocarbons will exist in reasonable quantities. There won't be so much of these that disposable plastic bottles, shopping and trash bags, and junk of all sorts overwhelms the settlements. Disposables may be cheap today as long as there is oil, and they might make a lot of money for some people, but what is the cost of cleaning up all the plastic pollution there is today? Space settlement environments won't be large enough to handle all kinds of trash. Some discarded plastics will be melted down and molded into new products and others will be reduced to their constituent elements of hydrogen, nitrogen, carbon, chlorine and sulfur in plasma arc furnaces.

Small numbers of miners could operate swarms of robots that dig up C-type asteroid material and roast it in electric or solar furnaces to drive out the water and hydrocarbons. The water and hydrocarbons could be loaded into robotic tankers, even supertankers, propelled by nuclear rockets or just light sails and magnetic sails, for delivery to customers all over the solar system. On Titan, liquid hydrocarbons could be pumped up, loaded into jet-atomic vehicles, and rocketed up to orbit where the liquids are transferred to interplanetary tankers. When all the economically recoverable oil on Earth has been extracted and the petroleum industry is no more, Big Oil might experience a new renaissance in outer space with carbonaceous asteroid mining and liquid methane extraction on Titan. Massive robotic supertankers might navigate all over the solar system with their cargoes of hydrocarbons. If a population of a trillion humans with lifespans of several centuries emerges in the solar system someday, there will be big money in hydrocarbons, chemicals and products made from them. They won't be used for fuel. Hydrogen could be the fuel of outer space, or more accurately, the working fluid for nuclear rockets. Supplying all the hydrogen demanded by a trillion space travelers would probably mean mining the atmospheres of the giant planets with balloon born robotic factories or jet-atomic ram scoops. Gargantuan liquid hydrogen tankers might travel all over the solar system too. The Rockefeller or Getti of outer space might become the richest man in the solar system.

Water could be big business too. A space settlement with a million people will demand a lot of water, even with recycling. Once the water is supplied it will be recycled but there could be leakage and the need for replacement. Water will come from C-type asteroids and ices on the moons of the outer planets. Hydrogen from the giant planets' atmospheres could be combined with the large quantities of oxygen that are the by-product of metal smelting for iron, magnesium and aluminum from stony asteroids to make water. Water tankers might consist of aluminized Kevlar balloons the size of the Hindenburg filled with water mounted on a metal truss with some kind of nuclear propulsion system.

Water, hydrogen, hydrocarbons could be some of the hottest commodities in space. When the need emerges, there will be businessmen and women who will fill that need. Each space settlement will be mostly self-sufficient, but there will be things that the local economy can't produce. Trade is the only way to get everything people need and want. If somebody has something to sell, she or he will have to advertise via the interplanetary internet. A complex network of telecommunication lasers will have to exist throughout the solar system. People will place orders, the sellers will fill those orders, and robotic freighters and tankers will deliver the goods. At the buyer's space settlement, packages will be unloaded at the spaceship dock and delivered to their doorstep by the local postal service or a private delivery company. Orders and payments will travel via radio or laser at light speed. Shipping might take months or years. Spaceship owners in the settlements will have to plan ahead and order spare parts and propellant long before they are needed.

A million people in a large O'Neill cylinder, half of them women, are going to want all kinds of things they can't get locally. There will also have to be interplanetary credit card companies and interplanetary banks. Transactions will all be electronic instead of paper. If there are any paper checks or paper money they will probably only be used locally inside the space settlement. The global network that makes these things possible today on Earth will have to grow out into the solar system. Perhaps the Martian settlers will get the money they need to terraform their world by selling all kinds of manufactured items to settlers in "free space." Given the low gravity of Mars it could be cheaper to rocket things up than it would be from Earth, and Mars is closer to the Main Asteroid Belt where most of the space settlements might exist. Of course, they will have to compete with solar orbiting space settlements where things are manufactured too, and that might be difficult given the low energy requirements for moving things from space settlement to space settlement. The constantly changing positions of planets, asteroids and settlements must also be considered. Sometimes it will be cheaper and faster to get something from Mars when it is in a good position to send out a ship and another space settlement has drifted to the other side of the Sun. A million people would probably order hundreds of products every day from the future interplanetary version of Amazon and shippers would have to load up combined orders. You can't send a space freighter out with just one pair or shoes on board!!! But it might be possible to ship special orders in small rockets the size of torpedoes. One must wonder what the price for something like that will be.

Money is only a medium of exchange. It has no real value unless goods and services are actually traded. There could be local currencies in space settlements and settlements on other bodies of the solar system that form independent political entities. Several universal currencies for interplanetary trade might exist. These may develop from the American dollar or the Chinese yuan, or they may grow out of digital cryptocurrencies.

Beyond the solar system, in settlements orbiting nearby stars and on the surfaces of exo-planets, independent economies will develop. If it takes 10 years for a radio or laser message to reach another solar system at the speed of light, and 50 or even 100 years for freighters to cross the interstellar gulf and deliver the goods, buyers will prefer locally sourced products from their own solar system, even if they are not exactly what they want. Sometimes you have to settle for second best. It doesn't seem as if interstellar trade will be practical as long as we are limited to travel at fractions of light speed. Information exchange via radio or laser might work, but not the buying and selling of physical goods. In the Star Trek universe, interstellar trade and tourism might be possible, but in the universe as we know it now, given the laws of physics we are aware of, it's not likely. Making everything on site is more reasonable. Travel to other star systems will probably be one way with the intention of settling and developing a distant system. Interstellar settlers will bring their robots and replicators with them and use asteroid, comet and planetary resources to build everything they need and want. Those destination star systems will be thoroughly mapped and studied by robot probes sent out decades earlier.

The business of interstellar settlement seems as if it will be more costly than settlement of our home solar system. Someone or some corporation will have to build massive solar energy collectors to power laser or particle beams to propel starships with light sails or magnetic sails out of the solar system. Those solar energy complexes might also be used to power particle accelerators for making anti-matter. Ships with magnetic scoops might be able to harvest hydrogen from the interstellar plasma and overcome the drag with thrust produced by anti-matter fueled engines that energize the scooped hydrogen. Interstellar pioneers will have to buy or build their own starships, buy anti-matter or propulsion beam services, travel to another system and use their robots, replicators and their own intelligence and labor to carve out homes in the new star system. It won't be cheap, but nothing is free nor does it appear out of nowhere by magic. Work is the only way to create things of value. That will be true even if we figure out how to travel through hyperspace at warp speed someday.

The Case Against the Moon

The case for Mars often involves the case against the Moon. Space enthusiasts hotly debate the Moon vs. Mars and much of their case for Mars is not based on the virtues of the red planet but their arguments against the Moon. I take no sides in this dispute. Clearly, we should be going to the Moon and Mars with exploration of Deimos and Phobos too.

It has been argued that Mars has a 24.5 hour day/night cycle and plants need a 24 hour day/night cycle. Earth days and Mars days are similar enough so that plants could be cultivated there, but the Moon has a 27.3 day cycle consisting of roughly two weeks of constant light followed by about two weeks of darkness. Plants cannot survive much less grow and reproduce given this lunar cycle. Moreover, sunlight on the Moon is unfiltered by the ozone layer and contains too much ultraviolet radiation for healthy crops. Cosmic rays and solar flare radiations will kill plants unless the greenhouses are made of glass so thick it will collapse even in low lunar gravity. In the bright sunlight of the lunar surface, without an atmosphere to screen out much of the infrared rays and no ozone layer to block the raw UV, greenhouses will super heat and the plants will die.

None of these arguments are valid. During the lunar day, light could be piped into below ground farm modules with fiber optic pipes and/or lens and mirror arrangements. Shutters could open and close to produce a 24 hour light/dark cycle. During the long lunar night, artificial illumination with microwave sulfur lamps or red and blue LEDs would keep the plants alive. Power for the lamps would come from banks of batteries or fuel cells charged up by solar panels during the lunar day. Small nuclear power plants, fueled possibly with U233 made from lunar thorium 232, could also be used. If a near polar location is chosen for a Moon base then almost constant sunlight is available with just a few days of darkness every month or so. Storing up energy for short periods of darkness near the poles would be a lot less challenging than storing up energy for two weeks of artificial illumination. As for the UV rays, the fiber optic pipes or reflector arrangements could have UV filters in them. Greenhouses would not be used. Farm modules covered with about 7 meters (about 23 feet) of lunar regolith will be shielded from cosmic rays and solar flares as well as thermal extremes and micrometeorites. If the intent of the base builders is Moon mining, there will be plenty of excavation equipment in place that could be used to shovel up regolith in low lunar G and cover inflatable farm modules. The air pressure in the modules would be high enough to support the layer of regolith shielding. Loose regolith is such a good thermal insulator that at a depth of just one meter in the equatorial regions of the Moon the temperature is a constant minus 20° C. (minus 4° F.). Seven meters of regolith will certainly make it possible to keep farm modules cool, and only enough light to support the crops will be piped in so there will be no overheating.

Lunar gravity is said to be too low for human health. However, Mars gravity is rather low too. Prolonged living in weightlessness on the ISS has shown that weightlessness is very bad for health. Nothing is known about the effects of partial gravity. Small rotating space stations with outer hubs producing Mars equivalent gravity and inner hubs with lunar equivalent gravity stocked with lab animals might provide us with the data needed to plan for our future on the Moon and Mars. The gravity issue does more to make a case for rotating one Gee O'Neill settlements rather than a case for Mars. Advances in bio-medical science and perhaps genetic engineering might make it possible for humans to thrive in partial gravity without bone and muscle atrophy or developmental defects. It might also be possible for Lunans and Martians to spend some of their time in centrifuges or in orbiting space settlements to get a therapeutic dose of "gravity" while living on the surface only part time to stay healthy.

Mars has an atmosphere of carbon dioxide and nitrogen mostly. It also has subsurface water ice and polar water ice and frozen carbon dioxide. These resources of light elements are vast compared to the light element resources of the Moon. This is true and it is one reason Mars is more likely to be a home for billions of humans someday if the red planet can really be terraformed and if humans can adapt to the low gravity. Even so, the Moon has enough hydrogen, carbon and nitrogen implanted by the solar wind in the regolith along with millions of tons of polar ices containing water, carbon oxides and ammonia to make it possible to build up industry on the Moon for solar power satellite construction and helium 3 mining. Eventually, asteroids will supply the Moon with all the light elements it needs and Mars could supply the Moon with copper, zinc and chlorine.

The Moon has commercial potential. It also has location, location, location. The Moon is only 3 days away or less. With space refueling ships could get there in only 30 hours. With chemical rockets it takes about six months to get to Mars. Nuclear propulsion systems might someday make it possible to reach Mars in two months or less. The Moon is a more attractive destination for tourists than Mars is. If millions of people could go to the Moon every year, and spend a few harmless weeks in low G, vacation company revenues could be in the trillions of dollars. Taking six months to reach Mars, then waiting about two years for a launch window and six months back to Earth would be too much for most travelers. It's more likely that Mars will be settled by hard-core pioneers who don't care how long it takes to get to Mars and it's likely they will travel one way and never return to Earth. That will require quite a commitment.

During a six month voyage to Mars a pioneer would soak up enough cosmic rays to significantly increase his or her chances of getting cancer. Perhaps there will be better treatments for cancer in the future, even vaccines to prevent the disease, and this won't be such a problem. The thin atmosphere of Mars does little to shield the surface from cosmic rays and solar flares. Martians could do the same thing their Lunan counterparts do and cover their habitat with several meters of regolith. They could also live underground in Martian caves and lava tubes.

Underground living will also protect Martians from thermal extremes. It gets cold as hell on Mars. Pro-Mars/Anti-Moon types cite the severe temperature extremes of the Moon vs. the more moderate, but still Antarctic, temperatures of Mars as a better reason to go to Mars. This is true, but there are ways of dealing with temperature extremes on both worlds. Regolith radiation shields will also provide thermal insulation and wise individuals would avoid traveling at night on Mars when it is very cold. Lunans would be wise to restrict travel during the heat of day and the cold of night too. Even so, spacecraft can be protected from thermal extremes and so can ground vehicles for the Moon and Mars.

The Moon will never be terraformed. In a thousand years or so it might be possible to go outside on Mars with just light clothing and breathe the air. Tourists may be visiting the Moon before the end of this century. Settling and terraforming Mars is in the more distant future. The Earth must be preserved first. Solar power satellites from lunar materials and lunar helium 3 may be needed to save civilization from climate change. We can wait a thousand years for Mars. By then, we might be settling Earth-like planets orbiting nearby stars.

If life spans are extended in the future, there will still be old age and death. The elderly, after a lifetime of wealth accumulation, might retire on the Moon, Mars or a rotating space settlement that only produces partial gravity to enjoy the benefits of low G. Less stress on painful arthritic joints and tired old muscles will be as desirable as luxury accommodations. Space retirement communities will be like fountains of youth. The Moon might be more popular than Mars because of its lower gravity and greater proximity to Earth. Others might prefer Mars because they like the looks of the place better. They might view the Moon as one big tourist trap while on Mars there will be people with horizons working to terraform that world. Some of the retirees might not be ready to be put out to pasture. They might want to work on the ice mining projects, water and carbon dioxide pipelines from the poles, fluorospar mines and greenhouse gas factories. Some might want to do scientific research into Martian geology and meteorology. When you are old, work can be the only thing that keeps you going.

Mars: Robots or Men?

Robert Zubrin's "Mars Direct" plan, sort of a minimalist dog sled to the North pole exploration strategy, has guts and imagination. I think the right crews could actually pull it off for a reasonable amount of money and do extensive surveys of Mars. What if they find something or some things of as much future value as lunar helium 3 will someday be?

Do we really need manned missions? There's a lot of danger involved from radiation to crash landings, burning up on re-entry, equipment failures that can't be repaired in flight or on Mars, not being able to produce enough propellant for return flight, etc. What if we used the Space Launch System (SLS) that is under development for a U.S. return to the Moon, or the Super Heavy/Starship, with a trans-Mars injection upper stage to send large automated probes to Mars instead of humans? With modern computers and AI, machines might do the job as well as humans did the job of exploring the Moon during the Apollo missions. Zubrin's Earth Return Vehicle (ERV) would have a mass of 28.6 metric tons. The Habitat module or Hab, would weigh 25.2 tons.[90] Certainly, we could send automated probes to Mars, aerobrake and parachute down to the surface, send out wheeled rovers and perhaps flying vehicles, do extensive exploration and load many soil and rock samples from various locations into the ERV for return to Earth where extremely detailed analysis could be done by scientists. If we could get some samples under microscopes we might answer the question, has there ever been life on Mars? What if there was once life on Mars? We know there was once liquid water. What if microbes and plankton lived in those seas, died, sank to the seafloors, formed sedimentary layers and even oil? Oil on Mars would definitely be proof of life teeming in the seas of Mars billions of years ago and it would make the prospects of successful human settlements even more likely.

The automated ERV could produce methane and oxygen for propellant to ascend from Mars and travel back to Earth. The possibility of back contamination from soil and rock samples in the ERV when it aerobrakes in Earth's atmosphere and splashes down is highly unlikely. There is far more danger from new viruses and bacteria evolving on Earth. The Hab wouldn't need a life support system or provisions of food, water and oxygen. It could contain two or more large rovers that can traverse hundreds of miles of Martian surface terrain and take samples as well as snap images. With smart enough robots and teleoperation from Earth, they could plant geophones and explosive charges to study the sub-surface of Mars. They could plant seismometers. The rovers, if they have enough range, and if we send enough missions to Mars, could plant a global network of seismometers that allows the study of Mars' interior. We wouldn't want to locate a manned based someday in a cave in a zone of high earthquake (or marsquake) activity, so we really need seismic maps of the red planet.

Imagine rovers that can travel several hundred miles on a tank of methane and a tank of LOX to power their fuel cells and electric motors. Over the course of a couple of years with this kind of exploration radius they could study vast areas on Mars. About six automated missions could really teach us a lot about Mars. We might locate suspected ore deposits of copper and zinc, and maybe uranium too. Discovering some fluorine bearing minerals would also be important for terraforming plans.

If we can launch such large payloads to Mars, we could also launch constellations of small "cubesats" in the nose of our Mars launchers, sort of like MIRVed warheads. The cubesats could form a GPS and telecommunication network for the rovers. We might also launch some orbital probes with powerful ground penetrating radars. Deep drilling rigs on some of the rovers could also obtain core samples for return to Earth. With a GPS system capable of locating a rover to within a few meters we could get exact locations for every sample. Heat flow probes might also be planted below ground. This could tell us about the future potential for geothermal power on Mars.

Once we have learned more about Mars, we could make better plans for future manned explorations and settlement. Exploring Deimos and Phobos should not be overlooked either. The moonlets of Mars might contain valuable resources for orbital construction and refueling facilities. It's very probable that the minerals these stony objects contain are largely oxygen like most typical silicate rocks. Liquid oxygen is the larger component of most liquid fuel rocket propellant combinations. Oxygen is necessary for breathing also, of course. There is a launch window to Mars, and a launch window to Deimos and Phobos, every 26 months. While many Near Earth Objects (NEOs) come so close to Earth that less delta velocity is needed to reach them than is needed to reach the Moon, the launch windows to or from these objects can be many years apart. Deimos and Phobos could provide useful materials every couple of years. Besides silicon and oxygen, the rocks of the moonlets certainly contain metals like iron and magnesium that could have all kinds of uses from habitat construction to solar reflectors. It was once hoped they would contain water and hydrocarbons like some carbonaceous asteroids, but this is now doubted. However, there is always the possibility that volatiles exist below their surfaces.

Orbital satellites could study the Martian weather. Rovers could plant small automated weather stations all over Mars, located precisely with GPS and linked to orbital communication cubesat constellations. We might learn to predict Martian weather. This is important because dust storms can wreak havoc by blotting out the Sun and covering solar panels with a layer of dust. Solar power would probably be used much of the time, but some nuclear power sources will also be needed. Small nuclear heating units will keep equipment warm at night. Nuclear power sources will also supply power all night long for radio systems, computers, propellant making equipment, battery recharging and more. Enough hydrogen has to be sent to Mars to make methane propellant for the ERV from atmospheric CO_2, and for rover power, unless the rovers have nuclear power.

Flying vehicles, drone helicopters, balloons and even small drone airplanes, could perform aerial photography for detailed mapping of vast territories. They might even contain radiation sensors that detect uranium and thorium deposits, and spectroscopes for analyzing the chemical content of the terrain. Magnetometers might yield some interesting data too. Advanced flying drones might even be able to locate interesting sites, land, and take samples for return to the ERV and Earth. Power could come from methane and LOX made on Mars that powers small internal combustion engines or fuel cells and electric motors for the propellers. They could also be fueled by CO_2 pumped down from the atmosphere that's used as reaction mass for small nuclear rockets. If the drones have their own compressor systems, combined with nuclear power, they would have virtually unlimited range for exploration.

Some real good AI that can be instructed to follow a certain route by controllers back on Earth and then carry out those instructions while using their own sensors and intelligence to avoid barriers and unexpected obstacles will be necessary. The robots will have to be smart enough to pick up rocks and dig up samples where ground controllers have instructed them to and store them onboard in separate bins without forgetting which sample is in which bin. They will have to be smart enough to load the sample bins into the ERV when the mission is ending. Given the amazing things done by Boston Dynamic's robots, it seems none of this will be beyond the ability of AI. The robotic rovers with their mechanical arms and eyes might even do maintenance and repair operations on themselves or each other. This would increase their odds of success.

Robotic exploration of Mars beyond that which is going on today might not excite the public as much as manned exploration, but it could provide as much data as humans could. Governments might fund these robotic explorations. Some people might want the government to stay out. With the success of SpaceX and Blue Origin rockets, private parties might do the job and keep their data secret except for paying customers. I don't believe in some kind of manifest destiny on Mars for the human race. Mars will belong to the people who expend their own blood, sweat and tears to pioneer that planet. Let's hope the failed experiment of socialism is dead by the time entrepreneurs settle the red planet, so there is no competition with governments and expenditures of taxpayer dollars. Governments have done lots of exploring already. It's time for the pilgrims, settlers and pioneers to open the frontier.

Space Energy: Reality Check

Chemical processes and metal smelting will be basic to space resource utilization and the creation of a space travel, tourism and real estate industry. Space energy will be the foundation for space industrial development and profit. Without space energy, it's hard to justify a massive investment. With space energy, it should be possible to make large profits and invest those in the expansion of space energy and other space industries.

If we can really build giant solar power satellites in reasonable amounts of time, they will still supply only a fraction of Earth's future energy demand. At present rates of growth, world civilization will require about 60 terrawatt years (TW) of energy by mid-century. However, two thirds of that is waste heat. If everything from cars and home furnaces to industrial processes and commercial buildings are completely electrified, we would need about 20 TW. Beyond mid-century, the population and energy demand might continue to grow.

If 5 GWe powersats are built, with masses of 5,000 to 50,000 metric tons, a thousand of them would be needed to provide 5 TW or 25% of Earth's energy demand in 2050 A.D. if everything is electrified. It's doubtful that a thousand powersats could be built by then even if we started today. If it was possible to build ten per year, and we got started in 2050 A.D., we would have a thousand of them by 2150 A.D. By then, electrical power demand might be 40 or 50 TW. Space solar power could only supply a fraction of that. Every other form of energy would also be needed including ground based solar, winds, storage, tides, waves, ocean currents and thermal energy conversion, hydro dams, geothermal, biofuel and waste burning, fusion and perhaps nuclear fission.

If fusion proves to be economical, there will be no shortage of deuterium since it is present in seawater, but tritium supplies may be limited. Second generation fusion reactors might fuse deuterium with deuterium. Third generation reactors could burn deuterium and helium 3. Helium 3 will be needed by the ton but it will only be possible to mine 33 kg. per square kilometer of lunar surface area. It seems we will need to mine thousands of square kilometers on the Moon every year. Lunar industry will have to mine for raw materials and build thousands of helium 3 mining machines weighing several tons each on the Moon. Large quantities of hydrogen, carbon and nitrogen will result as an added benefit. Even so, lunar helium 3 could supply only a fraction of future energy demand. Space energy is not the be all and end all of energy production. It will not put all other forms of energy production out of business. It will only supplement ground based energy production and net large profits for space energy corporations.

The giant planets of the outer solar system have endless amounts of helium 3 in their atmospheres. Space industry could grow to the point at which robotic mining ships could be sent to those worlds to extract helium 3 from their atmospheres with balloon borne harvesters or jet-atomic ram scoops. It might take years for the ships to reach the outer planets, years to mine and years to return to Earth with their bounty of helium 3. Decades of development in space might be needed to reach a time when such ships could be built and fueled.

Rockets like the SpaceX Super Heavy and Starship might get the cost to orbit down to $67 a kilogram. After reaching LEO, more flights would be needed to refuel the upper stages to propel them with their cargoes of powersat parts to GEO where mostly robotic stations are placed to assemble them. That will all add to the cost. At $67 per kilogram it will be much cheaper to orbit payloads bound for the Moon than it would be with SpaceX Falcon Heavy rockets. In my book, Mining the Moon: Bootstrapping Space Industry, I calculated that about $10 billion would be needed to transport a thousand tons of cargo placed in LEO with Falcon Heavies along with the solar electric ion tugs, one-way landers and propellant needed to get that cargo to the lunar surface. Super Heavy and Starship could knock a few billion dollars off that price tag. As for the future or Blue Origin rockets, that's unknown at this time.

Materials mined on the Moon and launched with mass drivers could be delivered to GEO for just a few dollars per kilogram. Those materials could be used to bootstrap powersat assembly stations in GEO to reduce the amount of cargo that has to be rocketed up from Earth. Building powersats with lunar materials would be far less costly than rocketing all their parts up from Earth. The high initial investment in lunar infrastructure would be worthwhile. Since the Moon lack elements like gallium, arsenic, indium and selenium, high efficiency solar cells would be rocketed up from Earth and installed on powersat frame and reflector assemblies made of lunar materials. With the Super Heavy/Starship or a Blue Origin equivalent that would become much more economical.

Lunar materials could also be used to build orbital space stations, space factories that make use of microgravity and free vacuum, spaceships and supply propellant to those spaceships. Space stations could be built for research purposes and they could also be built for hotels, casinos, recreation and real estate. Time shares and condominium could be built in some of the space stations. At a few dollars per kilogram for steel, cement and glass, it will be far cheaper to use lunar materials to build those orbital stations than to rocket everything up from Earth's surface with huge reusable rockets. Spaceships would require aluminum, magnesium and titanium which are available on the Moon. Oxygen for propellant is also plentiful in lunar regolith and rocks. Silicon for silane fuel is also abundant.

Back on Earth, an extensive amount of infrastructure development will be necessary. It took a hundred years to build the power grid that exists today in the developed nations and it will take some time, which I can only guess at, to expand the grid for electrification of all things using fossil fuels today and to electrify the Third World or less developed nations where two billion people have no electricity today. Even with climate change looming, it's probable that the poor countries will use cheap fossil fuels to climb out of their backward situation. In any case, electricity from space will be of no use if there are no power grids to deliver that energy in the quantities necessary to get away from fossil fuels. Solar power satellites require ground based receiving antennas (rectennas) connected to the grid. War in space is unlikely, although more advanced nations could attack powersats with missiles, but ground wars could still destroy rectennas, invertor stations that convert D.C. from space to A.C., and other parts of the electrical grid. Helium 3 will be useless without fusion reactors that can "burn" the stuff, and the cost of those reactors cannot be predicted.

Electricity won't sell in the less developed nations if they don't have homes and businesses with electric lights, air conditioners, computers, TVs, electric kitchens and appliances, etc. Factories, steel mills and cement making must all be electrified. Factories can use electric heat to melt metal for casting and glass. Steel mills could use electrically heated hydrogen and carbon monoxide to make pig iron and the by-product water and CO_2 could be recycled to make more hydrogen and carbon monoxide. Cement making could be electrified and CO_2 from limestone roasting could be captured and stored underground or used to make chemicals. With their populations growing, the poor countries won't want to wait for an ample supply of cheap, renewable electricity. They will use fossil fuels and add to the climate change problem. A quantum leap from cheap fossil fuels to a modern power grid with enough capacity to power electric cars and electric everything with power from 100% renewables does not seem likely. It's not impossible either.

Space energy in the near future is unlikely. If the investment was made today, we might have a lunar mining base and GEO construction stations in 20 years. I just don't think anyone is going to try to do the job without more real world demonstrations of the necessary technology in orbit and on the Moon. As of this writing, the Super Heavy/Starship has yet to successfully complete an orbital flight. The upper 1% have a total wealth of about $150 trillion. The money to industrialize space exists. Governments might attempt it. They could form a Space Power Authority and make money selling electricity to pay off their bond holders, reduce the national debt and save social security. The only problem with this approach is that it will stifle free enterprise in space.

A realistic approach to space energy, industry, tourism and settlement should temper enthusiasm for manned space flight. Billionaires might make orbital flights as they have already made sub-orbital flights, but that's not going to help save us from climate change and petroleum exhaustion. Coastlines might change and rain fall patterns could be altered in ways that help some and harm others. Realistically, we can switch from fossil fuels to renewables including space energy before we have extracted all the oil, coal and natural gas we can and alter the climate in such a way that the Greenland and Antarctic glaciers melt and raise the sea level by hundreds or just tens of feet and flood out vast regions and many major cities. Detractors may claim that temperatures are only going to rise a couple of degrees; however, the poles are warming faster and that's what we really have to be afraid of.

Lunar Money Matters

How much would it cost to build a bootstrapping base on the Moon for supplying materials for solar power satellite construction and other projects on the Moon and in orbit? We can make some estimates. A corporation would have to be formed that was capitalized by private multi-billion dollar fortunes, large international companies and by the sale of stocks and bonds. Research and development of all hardware and software would be required. That alone might cost one or two billion dollars.

If the initial batch of equipment, the "lunar industrial seed," weighs in at 1000 tons and a Falcon Heavy can put 53 tons in LEO for $90 million, the cost of orbiting the seed would be $1.7 billion.

1000/53 = 18.87 or 19 actual launches. 19 X $90 million = $1.71 billion

By comparison, the Space Shuttle could orbit 30 tons for $450 million to $1.6 billion.[91] The cost of the actual equipment might be one or two billion dollars. So now we are at $3.7 billion to $5.7 billion.

Transporting the "seed" to the Moon will not be cheap. Solar electric cargo tugs will have to be orbited and they will need propellant although not a lot compared to chemical rockets. We can estimate that the tugs and their hydrogen, argon or xenon propellant loads will total about 300 tons or 30% as much as the payload mass. Orbiting those would cost about $540 million.

300/53 = 5.66 or 6 actual launches 6 X $90 million = $540 million

The solar electric tugs would move the cargo modules from LEO to LLO over the course of several months, maybe up to a year.

Landers and space storable hypergolic propellant to move the cargo from low lunar orbit (LLO) to the lunar surface would be needed. That could add up to another 1500 tons to LEO that then has to be moved to LLO. It would cost about $2.6 billion to put this in orbit. We are now looking at about $6.8 billion to $8.8 billion.

This estimate did not come out of thin air. We can use the rocket equation to determine that with hypergolic propellant fueled lander rockets with specific impulses of about 315 seconds and a delta V of 1.8 km/sec to descend from LLO and disposable one way landers that weigh about 20% as much as the 1000 ton lunar industrial seed, about 950 tons of propellant is needed. To move this mass of 1150 tons to LLO we can estimate that 30% of that for solar electric cargo tugs will bring the grand total for tugs, landers and propellant for landing 1000 tons of actual cargo is just about 1500 tons.

Isp 315 X 0.0098 = 3.087 km./sec.

$e^{(v/c)} = e^{(1.8/3.087)} = 1.79$ (1.79)(1000 + 200) = 2148   2148-1200 = 948

948 + 200 ~ 1150 (0.3)(1150) = 345   1150 + 345 = 1495 or about 1500

1500/53 = 28.3 or 29 actual launches   29 X $90 million = $2.61 billion

Landers without propellant onboard that weigh only 20% as much as their payloads seems like a stretch. Unlike a manned lunar lander that has two even three stages for descent, ascent and orbital rendezvous these landers would have one stage, travel one way and be expendable. They would consist merely of fuel and oxidizer tanks made of lightweight 8000 series lithium-aluminum alloy or composite materials along with a small rocket engine. They would not have landing gear but only airbags inflated by rocket motor exhaust. Upon touchdown the landers would probably be crushed by the heavy cargo modules they are attached to. They could then be scavenged for materials. The cargo modules containing the actual payloads of machines, supplies and any packing materials would also be scavenged. Nothing can go to waste in the austere environment of the Moon.

What if the Super Heavy/Starship was used?

1000 tons cargo + 300 tons ion tugs + 1500 tons landers, propellant and more tugs = 2800 tons   2800/150 = 18.67 or 19 launches @ $10 million

= $190 million versus $4.85 billion using Falcon Heavy rockets.

The Super Heavy and Starship could save $4.66 billion. That could be spent on R & D, operations, and the big expense of moving humans into space.

There would also have to be ground stations for tracking and control and that would add cost. A wild guess is that about $10 billion would be involved. There might be ways to reduce costs. An exhaustive study could be done to determine exactly how much cargo for the lunar industrial seed would really be needed to build up a full-fledged mining base. Perhaps only a few hundred tons of cargo rather than a thousand tons as I have speculated would be needed. If NASA builds a base in the south polar regions of the Moon and successfully mines ice, that ice could be used to make propellant for reusable landers that shuttle cargoes down from LLO to the base site. The best place to put a mass driver launcher on the Moon seems to be at 33.1 degrees east on the lunar equator.[92] If NASA can supply lander propellant to a commercial mining and mass driver base on the equator for a reasonable price over a billion dollars might be saved.

How much money can the base earn? At $2 per kilogram launched by mass driver with mass catchers expelling about 500,000 tons of reaction mass for delivering 600,000 metric tons of lunar material annually, that's $1.2 billion per year. It would take about 8.33 years to break even if $10 billion is spent. An extensive amount of space industry would have to exist. Solar power satellites are the only way to make a business case for lunar industrialization. When we consider that a 5GWe space solar power satellite selling electricity at 2 cts./ kWhr could earn revenues of $867 million annually and $2.19 billion annually at 5 cts./kWhr, everything appears to be more lucrative. Wholesale electricity is sold for about 5 cts./kWhr today and retail goes for 10 to 11 cts./kWhr. In some places, like Germany and California, retail electricity is even more expensive. Space solar power satellites could earn substantial profits selling power to developed nations and still earn plenty selling cheap electricity to developing nations. Global living standards could be improved without resorting to large scale burning of cheap fossil fuels in developing nations.

Space industry, energy and settlement will not be the boondoggle some people may think it is when cheap clean power is delivered to the Earth. The real travesty would be continuing to burn coal for electricity in ever larger amounts with no concern about climate change, acid rain and other adverse effects on the environment and human health due to the emission of radionucleides, particulates, heavy metals, mountains of coal ash, carcinogens, ozone, NOx and SO_2. Moon mining and SSPSs are not the end of the story. Tourism, space manufacturing, space real estate and other enterprises could lead to substantial financial gains. Wealthy space condominium and time share owners will not be the only people who enjoy the final frontier. Many people will go to work in space and some of them could become permanent citizens of space. Eventually the price of space travel will fall and a mass market will evolve. No doubt there will be plenty of pioneers who don't care about NW Canada, Siberia or Antarctica who emigrate out into the solar system.

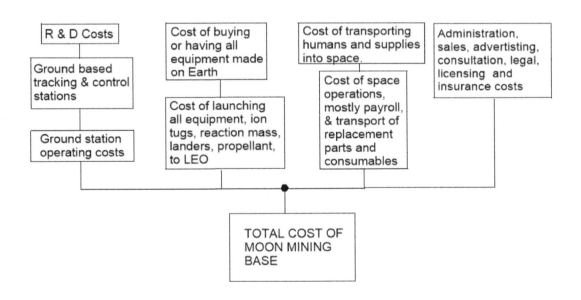

. Fig. 12 Flow chart of cost items contributing to price of a lunar industrial base

References

1) Matthew E. Gajda. A Lunar Volatiles Miner, May 2006 [M.S. thesis]. UWFDM-1304 https://fti.neep.wisc.edu/fti.neep.wisc.edu/research/he3.html

2) Dr. Peter J. Schubert. Energy Resources Beyond Earth-SSP from ISRU. November 2014. https://ildwg.files.wordpress.com/2015/03/energy-resources-beyond-earth-ssp-from-isru-schubert.pdf

3) Advanced Automation for Space Missions. Edited by Robert A. Freitas, Jr. and William P. Gilbreath. Pg. 290. Santa Clara, CA.1980. https://space.nss.org/media/1982-Self-Repliacting-Lunar-Factory.pdf

4) Dr. William Agosto. "Lunar Beneficiation." http://www.nss.org/settlement/nasa/spaceresourcesvol3/lunarben1b.htm

5) Matthew E. Gajda et. al. "A Lunar Volatiles Miner." Nasa-academy.org/soffen/travelgrant/gajda.pdf

6) Decomposition of Carbon Dioxide. http://carbon.atomistry.com/decomposition_carbon_dioxide.html

7) Boudouard Reaction. https://en.wikipedia.org/wiki/Boudouard_reaction

8) Lunar Geology: Minerals on the Moon-PERMANENT. https://www.permanent.com/lunar-geology-minerals.html

9) Robert Zubrin. The Case for Mars. Pg. 196. Touchstone, NY: 1996.

10) Robert Zubrin. The Case for Mars. Pg. 182. Touchstone, NY: 1996.

11) Geoffrey A. Landis. "Materials Refining on the Moon." Acta Astronautica 60. Pg. 906. 2007. Available < http://taniwha.org/~bill/Landis.pdf >

12) Geoffrey A. Landis. "Calcium Reduction as a Process for Oxygen Production from Lunar Regolith." AIAA. 2011. Available: <https://www.researchgate.net/publication/268566238_Calcium_Reduction_as_a_Process_for_Oxygen_Production_from_Lunar_Regolith >

13) Copper. https://en.wikipedia.org/wiki/Copper#Applications

14) Chloride-bearing deposits on Mars. en.wikipedia.org/wiki/Chloride-bearing_deposits_on_Mars

15) NASA Science: https://solarsystem.nasa.gov/asteroids-comets-and-meteors/asteroids/in-depth/#many_shapes_and_sizes_otp

16) https://en.wikipedia.org/wiki/Asteroid_belt

17) https://en.wikipedia.org/wiki/Carbonaceous_chondrite

18) https://en.wikipedia.org/wiki/Asteroid_mining

19) Universe Today. https://www.universetoday.com/37425/what-are-asteroids-made-of/

20) Advanced Automation for Space Missions. Edited by Robert A. Freitas, Jr. and William P. Gilbreath. Chp.4.2.2 Table 4.16 Lunar Factory Applications of Processed Basalt. Santa Clara, CA.1980. http://en.wikisource.org/wiki/Advanced_Automation_for_Space_Missions/Chapter_4.2.2

21) Linus Pauling. General Chemistry. Dover Publications, Inc. New York. Pg. 644,1988

22) Rudolph Keller and David B. Stofesky. "Selective Evaporation of Lunar Oxide Components." Space Manufacturing 10. AIAA and SSI. 1995. Abstract: https://space.nss.org/space-manufacturing-10/

23) What Are the Proper Concrete Mix Proportions? BN Products. http://www.bnproducts.com/blog/what-are-the-proper-concrete-mix-proportions/

24) https://www.engineeringnotes.com/concrete-technology/sulphur-concrete/sulphur-concrete-production-properties--and-advantages-concrete-technology/31868

25) Linus Pauling. General Chemistry. Dover Publications, Inc. New York. Pg. 636,1988

26) Formaldehyde. https://en.wikipedia.org/wiki/Formaldehyde

27) Ethane. https://en.wikipedia.org/wiki/Ethane

28) Heat Pipe. https://en.wikipedia.org/wiki/Heat_pipe#Spacecraft

29) Methanol to Olefins
http://www.cchem.berkeley.edu/molsim/teaching/fall2009/mto/background.html

30) Su, J., Zhou, H., Liu, S. *et al.* Syngas to light olefins conversion with high olefin/paraffin ratio using $ZnCrO_x$/AlPO-18 bifunctional catalysts. *Nat Commun* **10,** 1297 (2019). https://doi.org/10.1038/s41467-019-09336-1

31) Darrel D. Ebbing and Mark S. Wrighton ed. General Chemistry 14th edition, pg. 936. Houghton Mifflin Company. Boston.1993

32) ditto, pg. 651

33) Acetone. https://brittanica.com/science/acetone

34) Acetone. https://en.wikipedia.org/wiki/Acetone#Chemical_intermediate

35) Acetone. https://en.wikipedia.org/wiki/Acetone#Current_method

36) Bakelite. https://en.wikipedia.org/wiki/Bakelite

37) Schuhmann, M. et al. "Aliphatic and aromatic hydrocarbons in comet 67P/Churyumov-Gerasimenko seen by ROSINA." 2019.
https://ui.adsabs.harvard.edu/abs/2019A%26A...630A..31S/abstract

38) Preparation of Benzene-Aromatic compounds in Organic Chemistry.
https://byjus.com/chemistry/preparation-of-benzene

39) Calcium Carbide. https://en.wikipedia.org/wiki/Calcium_carbide

40) Geoffrey A. Landis. "Resource Production on the Moon." 5th Joint Meeting of Space Resources Roundtable/Planetary and Terrestrial Mining Sciences Symposium, Golden, CO. June 10-11, 2014.
https://ntrs.nasa.gov/archive/nasa/casi.ntrs.nasa.gov/20140017767.pdf

41) Vinyl Chloride. https://en.wikipedia.org/wiki/Vinyl_chloride

42) 1,2 Dichloroethane. https://en.wikipedia.org/wiki/1,2-Dichloroethane

43) Polyvinyl Chloride. https://en.wikipedia.org/wiki/POlyvinyl_chloride

44) https://en.wikipedia.org/wiki/Haber_process

45) https://www.statista.com/statistics/974691/us-benzene-production-volume/

46) https://en.wikipedia.org/wiki/Terephthalic_acid

47) https://patents.google.com/patent/US4101595A/en

48) https://repository.upenn.edu/cgi/viewcontent.cgi?article=1006&context=cbe_sdr

49) Aniline. https://en.wikipedia.org/wiki/Aniline

50) https://en.wikipedia.org/wiki/Cyclohexane

51) https://www.researchgate.net/publication/226332671_Industrial_Catalytic_Aspects_of_the_Synthesis_of_Monomers_for_Nylon_Production

52) https://en.wikipedia.org/wiki/Styrene

53) https://en.wikipedia.org/wiki/Alkylbenzene_sulfonates

54) https://www.masterclass.com/articles/rayon-fabric-guide#what-is-rayon

55) https://en.wikipedia.org/wiki/Ethenone

56) William H. Nebergall and Frederic C. Schmidt. College Chemistry. Pg. 445. D.C. Heath and Co., Boston 1957.

57) Glycerol. https://en.wikipedia.org/wiki/Glycerol

58) Castor Oil. https://en.wikipedia.org/wiki/Castor_oil

59) Jojoba Oil. https://en.wikipedia.org/wiki/Jojoba_oil#History

60) New Production Process Makes PLA Bioplastic Cheaper and Greener. New Atlas. https://newatlas.com/bioplastic-pla-cheaper-production-process/38498/

61) https://polymerinnovationblog.com/from-corn-to-poly-lactic-acid-pla_fermentation-in-action/

62) https://www.wikihow.com/Make-Bioplastic

63) https://www.wikihow.com/Make-Paper-at-Home

64) https://boltthreads.com/technology/mylo/

65) https://boltthreads.com/technology/microsilk/

66) Bamboo. https://en.wikipedia.org/wiki/Bamboo

67) Bamboo Textiles. https://en.wikipedia.org/wiki/Bamboo_textile#Bamboo_rayon

68) https://www.thoughtco.com/drugs-and-medicine-made-from-plants-608413

69) https://www.diynatural.com/natural-fabric-dyes/

70) https://thegreenhubonline.com/2018/05/16/easy-diy-how-to-dye-fabric-using-natural-vegetable-dyes/

71) Carbonaceous Chondrite. https://en.wikipedia.org/wiki/Carbonaceous_chondrite

72) https://en.wikipedia.org/wiki/Surgical_suture

73) https://www.acsh.org/news/2016/12/28/semisynthetic-real-word-saves-lives-10605

74) https://en.wikipedia.org/wiki/Cyclohexane

75) ditto

76) https://en.wikipedia.org/wiki/Cyclohexanone

77) https://en.wikipedia.org/wiki/Nylon

78) https://textilelearner.net/spandex-fiber-properties-manufacturing/

79) https://en.wikipedia.org/wiki/Isocyanate

80) https://en.wikipedia.org/wiki/Phosgene

81) https://en.wikipedia.org/wiki/Polyurethane

82) https://en.wikipedia.org/wiki/Aniline

83) https://en.wikipedia.org/wiki/4,4%27-Methylenedianiline

84) https://en.wikipedia.org/wiki/Polyethylene_terephthalate#Production

85) https://en.wikipedia.org/wiki/Neoprene

86) https://en.wikipedia.org/wiki/Chloroprene

87) https://en.wikipedia.org/wiki/Butadiene

88) Geoffrey A. Landis. "Materials Refining on the Moon." Acta Astronautica 60 pg. 913. 2007. Available:

< http://taniwha.org/~bill/Landis.pdf >

89) https://en.wikipedia.org/wiki/Fiberglass

90) Robert Zubrin. The Case for Mars. pg.93. Touchstone, NY:1996

91) https://www.nasa.gov/centers/kennedy/about/information/shuttle_faq.htm#1

92) T. A. Heppenheimer. Colonies in Space. Chp.6-The Moon Miners. 1977,2007. https://space.nss.org/colonies-in-space-chapter-6-the-moon-miners/